Marilyn Luscombe was born in Sheffield in 1945.
Educated at St Hugh's College, Oxford and the
Institute of Archaeology, Oxford, she has worked in
Public Relations and is now an archaeological
archivist at the British Museum. She began
bodybuilding in 1981 and went on to win a number
of regional championships as well as being a finalist
in two British championships. She has taught
women's bodybuilding courses at the Fitness Centre
and Central YMCA in London, and written articles
for various fitness magazines, such as *Work-Out* and
Bodybuilding Monthly, and also talked on radio and
TV about women's bodybuilding.

Marilyn Luscombe

DESIGNER BODY

PANTHER
Granada Publishing

Panther Books
Granada Publishing Ltd
8 Grafton Street, London W1X 3LA

Published by Panther Books 1985

Copyright © 1985 Marilyn Luscombe

ISBN 0-586-06421-4

Printed in Great Britain by St Edmundsbury Press,
Bury St Edmunds, Suffolk

Set in Century Schoolbook

Für E.H.S.
 in Liebe, Freundschaft
 und Bewunderung

'To become a winner you need to adopt a set of values and the ability to discipline yourself, and you can carry those values over to the rest of your life, so that you can do everything better.'

Arnold Schwarzenneger,
seven times 'Mr Olympia'

ACKNOWLEDGMENTS

I wish to thank Carolyn Cheshire for kindly agreeing to give her blessing to the contents of my book by introducing it.

I owe a particular debt of gratitude to Mike Down, BA, MSc, MPhys Ed, Founder President of the EFBB, and a leading expert in sports science and nutrition. He has given generously of his time and efforts to read the typescript and made many detailed and constructive comments. In addition, he has also given me practical help, advice, and encouragement as a competitor on many occasions in the past; as have my many other friends at Downs Fitness Centre, Bristol.

My thanks and appreciation also to Howard Payne, Lecturer in the Mechanics of Sport at Birmingham University (official photographer for the AAA) and distinguished Olympic and international hammer thrower, who read through my text and offered detailed criticism and factual correction and made many useful suggestions for improvement.

I should like to thank especially Alastair Morrison, who has collaborated with me to produce the exercise photographs in a most sympathetic spirit. I think the excellent results admirably demonstrate his light touch and professionalism.

Miss Louisa Komzolik typed endless pages from my rough and ready manuscript with speed and efficiency. By keeping pace with my writing, she kept me under pressure to carry on in often adverse circumstances. My aunt, Miss Betty Tilley, ably assisted by proof-reading the drafts and offered frequent practical help and support.

My editor Judith Kendra of Granada Publishing and literary agent, Anthony Goff, I cannot thank enough for their hard work, continuing support and advice, practical aid and encouragement, and gently applied pressure when necessary. They have made it all seem deceptively easy to write and produce a complex book. I hope that my efforts justify their confidence in me and I am conscious that any defects are entirely mine.

GENERAL ACKNOWLEDGMENTS

Photos not by Alastair Morrison:

Geoff Collins (official EFBB photographer)
Keith Kimball

For location photography:

The Dave Prowse Fitness Centre
12 Marshalsea Road
Borough
London
SE1

Bodywork Gym
Earlham Street
London
WC1

The Fitness Centre
Floral Street
Covent Garden
London
WC2

Leotards:

Bridget Woods

FOREWORD

by Carolyn Cheshire

A few years back, I was assisting with the promotion of the first 'Stars of Tomorrow', a bodybuilding contest aimed at attracting newcomers to the sport. Round about that time I met a great enthusiast, someone desperately eager to succeed in the sport. It was Marilyn Luscombe. But Marilyn was a little unusual for a bodybuilding *ingénue*. She was more mature than the average newcomer; she was an Oxford graduate and a professional academic.

Marilyn placed second in that contest and was sufficiently encouraged, from then onwards, to immerse herself in the sport. Her bodybuilding interests were not always popular with all concerned and her employers tried hard to discourage her.

She persisted, however, and in this book she has amalgamated her research skill and her education with her favourite pastime. Drawing on all the available resources, Marilyn has produced a unique book. It is the first instructional guide by a British woman bodybuilder, not only for her peers but for everyone. It cannot fail to amuse and inform even those with only the most fleeting of interest. So if you have ever thought about sculpting your own body, pick it up, take it home, and read it from cover to cover.

AUTHOR'S PREFACE

In 1980, when I started weight-training, very few people in Britain had even heard of bodybuilding for women. Training advice and facilities were very hard to come by. There was no obvious written source of information to consult, other than expensive imported American magazines and books and a scatter of male-orientated home-produced muscle magazines.

In writing this book, I set out to produce the sort of basic handbook which would have been invaluable to me at the start of my own training. It represents a synthesis of much that I have learned about the sport in the past four years from training and competing, from extensive reading, avid questioning, and teaching women's bodybuilding to beginners.

I do not profess to be an expert on the subject, for there is something new to learn every day about this highly complex sport. I write merely as someone who has tried it, and found out from experience what worked for her. I have also acquired some insight into the kind of questions women repeatedly ask and common misconceptions which arise.

I hope that this book, while far from being an exhaustive textbook, will provide a starting point and an inspiration for any woman to try bodybuilding for herself. It provides the necessary basic information in easily understandable form for her to progress from rock-bottom beginner to international competitor, if she should so aspire, or, if not, just to keep herself in shape and looking outstandingly good at any age.

It is up to you, the reader, to supply the motivation and self-discipline to succeed. There are no overnight transformations. Bodybuilding takes time and hard work. If that scares you, seek an easier option. If on the other hand you are prepared to work hard and train consistently, this is the way to change your body shape completely, and maybe the rest of your life along with it. This book will help anyone starting now to progress faster and go further, so that the sport of women's bodybuilding continues to flourish.

I am greatly indebted to many dedicated and enthusiastic athletes from whom I have learned so much, but in particular to Carolyn Cheshire, for her unfailing inspiration and advice.

Bodybuilding has changed my life completely for the better. I hope it will do the same for you.

M. R. L.

London
June 1984

CONTENTS

Acknowledgments   vii

Foreword by Carolyn Cheshire   ix

Author's Preface   xi

1 What Bodybuilding Is All About   1

2 How to Start   11

3 Basic Principles of Weight-Training   21

4 Exercises   28

5 Beginners' and Intermediate Work-Outs   89

6 Advanced Training Methods and Work-Outs   100

7 Nutrition for Bodybuilding   113

8 Training and Dietary Cycles   137

9 Competitions   148

APPENDICES

1 The Language of Bodybuilding   167

2 Bibliography

   i. Bodybuilding and Weight-Training   171

   ii. Nutrition   172

3 Addresses   173

Chapter One

WHAT BODYBUILDING IS ALL ABOUT

THE CHANGING SHAPE OF WOMEN

There has probably never been a time when women have not wanted to change the appearance of their bodies. Clothing and underpinnings have provided women with the means of creating an illusion of perfection, according to the dictates of their day and age, and in pursuit of the 'body beautiful' they have squeezed into corsets, bound their breasts, worn stiletto heels, bustles and padded shoulders and have in turn concealed or exposed just about every area of the body. One feature common to most of this self-inflicted torture has been restriction of movement, the result of which often rendered women weak and defenceless. The eighteen-inch waist in Victorian and Edwardian times, corseted to suffocation point, meant pale, fainting women. Hobble skirts and high heels made it impossible to run away in a dangerous situation, so women had to be 'protected', and dependent on men.

The twentieth century brought about the most fundamental changes in history as far as women's appearance was concerned. The legacy of two World Wars, women's emancipation and the women's liberation movement have all been reflected in the freedom to dress without restriction. Just as behaviour changed, so did clothing. The very shapelessness of much modern dress emphasized the need for something rather more shapely to go inside. Unfortunately, the mass rejection of corsetry also released a mass of flabby flesh. The emphasis therefore changed from the covering of the body to the body itself, and in the 1960s this trend was exaggerated to the point where emaciation became fashionable and punitive dieting arrived in earnest. The fleshy, rounded appearance typified by female film stars of the 1940s and 1950s gave way to the androgenous, adolescent look. The attainment of such an 'ideal' was certainly beyond all but a handful of women and no doubt a great deal of frustration, dissatisfaction and ill health was caused as a result.

Fortunately, there was a backlash. The blonde, tanned 'golden girl' look which originated in California and Australia, typified by Olympic athletes such as Mary Rand and soon copied by film and TV stars, arrived in the late 1960s and 1970s. This trend heralded a more healthy female image and continues with increasing momentum in the fitness-conscious 1980s.

In the past five years, a totally 'new-look' woman has emerged – the female bodybuilder, whose curves and confidence rely on lean, hard muscle-tone* and strength, instead of the traditional soft, rounded fleshiness of women as stereotyped by men. Any pretty girl born with a naturally good shape can enter a beauty contest and do well, but the beauty of the bodybuilder is something quite separate. For the first time ever, it is a look created by hard work, heavy training, good diet and a disciplined lifestyle. It is not a type of beauty which depends on the chance inheritance of regular features or stunning eyes, for the whole body is systematically trained in order to redesign its shape and proportions.

Bodybuilders are not subject to the tyranny of traditional beauty, which will inevitably fade with the years. They cheat time by their possession of a youthful body image because if, in middle age, you can retain the slim lines of youth, you will be assumed to be years younger than you are. Instead of accepting her shape as good, bad or indifferent by sheer chance of heredity, a bodybuilder takes herself in hand and alters it in any way she chooses. Her body is developed as an individual, aesthetic creation.

As with any fashion, there are only a few innovative people who create a look and wish to go to extremes. Similarly, in any sport, only an élite few have the God-given genes, potential and application to become Olympic athletes or 'Miss

---

* Some of the terms used in this book will be unfamiliar. Please refer to the glossary, The Language of Bodybuilding, pp. 167–9.

Olympia' contestants. Yet the influence of these few leaders and role models, whether in dress, rock music or fitness training, filters down the line and eventually touches the lives of us all. Even the most resistant women, who are adamantly opposed to 'fashion', are no longer wearing crinolines or powdered wigs. Over the years fashion in clothes and body shapes has changed and will continue to do so, sometimes gradually, sometimes dramatically fast, reflecting social developments.

The developed muscularity and proud self-confidence of the female bodybuilder may shock some women now, but already the standard of beauty is changing in its wake and, without doubt, the new independent and assertive role of women in society has much to do with it.

Beauty queens now admit to weight-training. Models in advertisements and magazines are seen holding weights. Many TV and film stars rely on weights for their much-admired figures and obvious fitness. Their example affects the women who seek to emulate them and who want to preserve or regain their own figure, fitness and self-esteem. It is no longer enough for a woman to be passively concerned with her appearance, relying on cleverly-designed clothing or expertly applied make-up and hairstyling to conceal her weak points.

Today's concept of beauty is the kind that shines out from within, the radiant glow and clear skin which reflect good health, good body condition and a well-adjusted mental attitude. To achieve such a look, it is not enough to follow a rigorous diet, spend a few days at a health farm, or indulge in passive beauty treatments. If the 'future woman' wants to be lean, capable, independent and strong, she will need to work hard to achieve these aims. As our lives become more and more mechanized and our bodies are used less and less, there is a critical need for exercise as part of everyone's lifestyle. Increased leisure time needs to be filled with active forms of relaxation which dissipate stress, not extra indolence which feeds it. The alternative is illness, stress and untimely death.

Women's bodies were meant to be active. Restrictive social conventions and a male-dominated society have prevented women achieving their physical potential for centuries, yet as the freedom of their actions has increased during this century, so also has the sedentariness of their lifestyle and the richness of their diets, as well as an apparent general hatred of exercise instilled by horrible memories of 'gym', netball, hockey and so on at school.

In Ancient Greece, it was not so. In Sparta, women

were given the same tough training as men since they would become mothers of the next generation of warriors. Many also took part in athletics contests and in their own separate Olympic games. Today, in more primitive societies than ours, women work in the fields and undertake the heavy labour. But the higher up the social scale you go and the more affluent people become, the more servants are employed to do the women's physical work. Inertia and weakness reflect high social status and the idea of women as decorative ornaments, useful only for childbearing and rearing, gains ground. The epitome of this concept has been reached in modern Western life where gadgets, convenience products and cars are so widely available that heavy labour, and sometimes even walking, are infrequent. On the rare occasions when extra physical demands are placed on the body, it cannot cope and develops back pain, pulled muscles and even heart attacks, since it has no reserves of strength, flexibility or stamina. In other words, it runs like a car with no top gear and, in an emergency, it lets you down.

The answer is obvious. Regular hard exercise is an absolute necessity in the modern world, particularly for women who have increasing demands made on them to run homes, raise families, hold down responsible jobs and, if possible, look fashionable at the same time, often all at once. There is no doubt in my mind that bodybuilding is the most comprehensive, effective and enjoyable exercise which best suits the needs of the modern woman and the new, interesting life she now leads.

WHY YOU NEED TO BE STRONG

In the course of everyday life, our muscles are normally used at a level way below their potential capacity for either strength or power. The majority of people have sedentary jobs and scarcely use their muscles at all. It is only when they engage in some infrequent heavy exercise that they suddenly develop aches and pains, since the undeveloped muscles are finally being used and scream out in agony as a result. Because of the intermittent nature of such efforts, the muscles never get the chance to become stronger in order to cope with the extra work and injuries such as torn muscles and back pain are almost inevitable.

The fact is, we all need strength and power in our everyday lives. Women often have to lift children, carry heavy shopping, move furniture around the house, give birth, carry heavy suitcases on holiday, dig the garden, and so on. It is no good expecting the body to be able to cope with such activities completely unprepared and it is certainly true that

whenever a strong man is required to help, there is never one available. If you wish to avoid being another statistic among the mass of back-pain sufferers crowding doctors' surgeries, then weight-training is the answer. To be strong is to be capable and independent.

WHY DIET ALONE IS NO GOOD

Diet alone can never give you a good-looking physique. A pear-shaped woman with little upper body development will end up looking scrawny and drawn around the face, shoulders and arms following a diet, but will still retain those resistant pockets of fat around her lower body. Fat always clings to the areas where it first accumulates. If that area happens to be your stomach, then before you see fat on the outside, you can be sure that there is already a thick layer inside your abdominal cavity. Diet can never be selective. Fat is generally lost in the same proportions all over the body. The only way that spot reduction can be achieved temporarily is by local water loss and, of course, once you have a drink, back it all goes again.

If a systematic long-term diet is employed, in combination with weight-training, then the fatty areas of the body will gradually reduce in size. Regular training will tone and build up the muscle underneath the fat. The result of this is that, as you lose bodyfat, the firm contours of newly-developed muscles will show through the skin, and the limbs will be more shapely than before. The actual measurement of your arm or leg may remain the same, but there is a world of difference between a flabby upper arm composed of bubbly fat, covered with gooseflesh skin, and a hard, toned limb, made up of shapely, lean and well-developed muscles, covered with healthy skin in good condition.

FEAR OF BUILDING MUSCLES

The appearance which most women seek is a lean, well-toned, feminine shape. Let us also add healthy and strong to that list, though these are not so often considered. No one could argue with the fact that this description is generally regarded as attractive by men and women alike, and that the exaggeratedly muscular, 'masculine' physique on a woman gets a wholehearted thumbs down.

It may therefore surprise you to know that the shape you so much admire depends on muscles. Muscles are not some extraneous, unwanted addition to the body caused by training with weights. Women want to lose weight by dieting but do not stop to think about what they will reveal once they become thin. Think about it – what is under the skin if you lose bodyfat and have undeveloped muscles? Only bones, veins and connective tissue – and these are singularly unattractive when sticking through paper-fine skin, which is why crash dieters look so terrible because their muscles have wasted away and they simply look drawn and ill. A bodybuilder should have no visible bones. When bodybuilders have the least possible bodyfat, their skeleton is covered with muscles, which give curvaceous and sensuous shape to their limbs.

The type of bodybuilder whose appearance scares the average, uninformed woman is usually a top competitor in peak condition for the contest, tanned, oiled and flexed on stage, posing in the most extreme manner possible to show off her development. But how often does anyone appear in everyday life in a bikini, performing a double biceps pose? Most of us only occasionally reveal ourselves in bathing wear, summer clothing or evening dress with our muscles relaxed. The average similarly dressed bodybuilder looks like a supremely healthy, curvaceous athlete, and nothing more threatening than that!

Many women are put off the idea of bodybuilding because they fear that it is unfeminine and will cause them to develop unsightly bulging muscles practically overnight. Believe me, building muscles is an extremely difficult and tough business. It takes a long time, intensive effort, specialized diet and relentless application. Competition shape is an exaggerated and ephemeral condition. No one can be in such prime condition for more than a few days or weeks each year, any more than an athlete could set a world record every day of the year. It takes so many months of specialized training and diet to achieve that most women will never approach such extremes. Compare the photographs taken of me demonstrating the exercises in this book while I was in off-season training, with the ones taken in peak competition shape on stage at the British Championships (pp. 5, 151, 152, 154). I think these will illustrate the difference.

You can stop weight-training at any point. All you have to do is keep an eye on the mirror. If you think a particular muscle group is becoming too developed and is noticeably out of proportion, then you can stop building it, and it will then decrease in size. For the woman who takes up weight-training for fitness and exercises lightly (less than three hours a week) the chances of gaining very much extra muscle are minute. What she will achieve is good muscle-tone – a hard, firm texture to the limbs, instead of soft, squashy fat.

Training with weights is hardly new. One of the most celebrated beauties of all time, the Empress Elizabeth of Austria, had a gym in her palace in Vienna where she worked-out daily in order to maintain her famous wasp waist. That was over a hundred years ago!

HOW BODYBUILDING CAN CHANGE YOUR SHAPE

Any activity which stresses one muscle group regularly, but not others, will result in uneven development. If you play tennis, you will develop one strong arm, swimming will give you well-developed shoulders, running firms the leg muscles, and so on.

When compared with other sports, only weight-training and specifically bodybuilding will enable you to reshape your individual physique any way you choose. The magic of body sculpture works by means of adding or subtracting muscle and fat in such a way that your proportions most closely approximate to the average woman's ideal. In most cases nowadays, this is the 'inverted triangle' physique, consisting of broad shoulders, a narrow waist, slim hips and long, firm, shapely legs. The average woman, however, tends to be the exact opposite, with narrow underdeveloped shoulders, not much waist, wide hips and thighs and too much lower body fat.

So what can bodybuilding do to improve her shape? Specific exercises can be applied to increase her shoulder width and build up her arms, chest and upper back. Her waist can be pulled in by a series of specialized exercises and her lower body slimmed and reshaped by means of a concentrated leg-exercise schedule. The whole programme should be combined with a sensible diet and some form of aerobic activity, all of which is described in this book.

HEALTH AND FITNESS BENEFITS

Most women will probably be attracted to weight-training by the prospect of improving their figures and, naturally, this is the most obvious benefit. However, there are other more important advantages. Top of the list is the general improvement in health which a regular training programme provides. I write from personal experience, having been a chronically sickly child and far from robust adult until I took up weight-training. Since then, I have had only a few colds and minor upsets and my general stamina and energy level has increased beyond recognition. The reason for this is two-fold. The circulation is improved, which, in turn, improves the functioning of the organs and also strengthens the immune

system. It is not only what you can see which is toned by working-out, but everything else inside you which you cannot see as well. In short, every system in the body operates more efficiently, including the digestive, nervous, endocrine, reproductive, cardio-vascular and respiratory systems and skeletal structure.

Cardio-Vascular System and Aerobic Conditioning

A heart–lung system which is operating properly means extra endurance. Some types of weight-training can be applied as an aerobic form of exercise. That is to say, the lungs and heart can be trained to take in oxygen more quickly and to transport it into the bloodstream and then into the muscles much more efficiently, so increasing stamina faster. An improvement in heart–lung efficiency is very important, for as weight-training work-outs become more advanced and longer, stamina and endurance are essential to enable the body to cope. In everyday life, sudden demands made on the body to run for a bus, climb stairs, or play ball with children will become much easier, instead of half killing you.

Any form of sustained, low-level aerobic exercise will use fat as its energy source by choice, and, at the same time, speed up the body's metabolic rate, making it ideal for a bodybuilder's pre-contest training programme.

The Basal Metabolic Rate (BMR) is the natural speed at which the body burns calories when at rest to provide its basic survival requirements. It can be speeded up, or slowed down, by one's activity level.

Aerobic exercise will not only speed up the basal metabolic rate but this rise will be sustained for 24 hours following an aerobic session, so if you can exercise aerobically every other day you will keep your bodyclock revving all the time. Short-term violent exercise, such as squash, will not have the same effect. Such sports call more on carbohydrate energy sources and do not force the body to draw on its fat reserves.

The Circulation and the Skin

Improved circulation carries oxygen-rich blood into the tissues and results in a healthy skin-tone – that glow which fit people always have. The blood is carried more efficiently around the body and waste products are eliminated faster. Blotchy patches, gooseflesh and spots will all gradually disappear, in conjunction with the correct diet, and so will accumulations of bubbly fat full of toxins, otherwise

known as 'cellulite'. The skin will tighten up as the muscles are toned beneath it and will not lose its elasticity so rapidly as the years pass. Wrinkles and stretchmarks will not appear as quickly and can be reduced if they already exist.

Better circulation can also improve the general level of warmth in the extremities and also help to improve mental alertness, hair growth and even eyesight.

The Nervous System

One of the great advantages of working-out regularly in a gym is that it gives you a couple of hours in the day which are yours alone. This time is neither work nor home life, but an oasis in between. I like to think of it as playtime, when it is possible to disappear from ordinary life and responsibilities and do one of the things you most enjoy, away from everyone to whom you owe duties. The element of escapism is in itself relaxing before you even begin working-out. I like to visit the gym between finishing work and going home, so that all the bugs in my system, created by the working day, are removed before I face the domestic scene.

Any exercise carried out regularly will affect the body beneficially by reducing stress levels. Pressure creates an unacceptable level of adrenalin in the body which, when it has no outlet, builds up into anxiety, depression and inertia, general weariness, debility and more serious forms of actual disease. Weight-training provides this important outlet by using up a great deal of energy and adrenalin. It is just impossible at the end of a heavy weight work-out to feel tense. The system is drained, but it is also relaxed. Runners are known to experience a 'high' at a certain point and this can also happen, to a lesser degree, during a long weight work-out.

There is no doubt that it is an exhilarating experience to push your body as far as it will go, stretch it to the limits of strength and endurance, and then to relax. Once you are fit, this is not exhausting but invigorating, unlocking reserves of energy you never knew were there. At the end of a really good work-out, you should feel like going out to do some dancing! And at the end of the day you will sleep better than you have ever done in your life before. Eventually, you will find you do not sleep well if you fail to exercise. It is the terrific 'high' that comes from a work-out, which eventually proves addictive for most people. It may be that your motives in the beginning are quite different, but the reason why people go back to the gym again and again is the feeling of exhilaration it provides, and the enormous increase in general energy levels which develops from it. Your body will, in fact, get used to the new level of activity and crave it.

Weight-training requires a great deal of concentration to perform well. Although there is a social element in going to a gym and seeing friends, once the work-out starts, all one's physical and mental faculties need to be marshalled and concentrated into achieving the objective. At the beginning, you may feel distracted, a bit down, tired, but after about 15 minutes the body warms up, the mind focuses, and a type of meditation takes over. Sometimes in the middle of a work-out, I am unaware of where I am, who is on the next bench, or of any other external factors. All my concentration is on the muscle I am operating and the exercise being performed. Sometimes it is necessary to be very aggressive in carrying out a difficult set, and the extra strength has to come from deep within, beyond the conscious barriers. The more concentration goes into the work-out, the more progress you make, and the more relaxed you feel at the end. A really bad irritant factor is a noisy gym, full of chatty people. I often begin a work-out in an aggressive mood. This is a deliberate marshalling of my negative energy to ensure extra power. As the work-out progresses and the adrenalin disperses, I become less tense, usually ending in a relaxed frame of mind. I actually find it hard to work-out really well if I am too happy!

In terms of everyday life, this type of training teaches the body and the mind to take on the extra load and cope with it. In other words, it raises your mental and physical breaking point. It makes you more aware of your body and its potential, and how to develop and control it. It not only gives you the extra physical strength to cope with everyday life but a reserve of mental strength too. It is something to know that you can discipline yourself to overcome the pain of a really hard set of exercises. It increases your confidence, self-discipline and willpower. All these factors will carry through into every other facet of your life and change your attitudes, together with the attitudes of others towards you. If you radiate confidence, fitness and success, these attributes will always attract the interest of other people of the same kind, so you exist in a much more positive environment. If doctors prescribed weight-training for depressed women, you could throw away most of the tranquillizers in Britain.

The Skeleton and the Muscles

If muscles are not used then they become weak and the same thing happens to the skeleton. If it is not exercised then the joints stiffen up, mobility is lost and aches and pains set in, leading in later life to arthritis and severe loss of mobility. Although there are hormonal changes as we age, and deterioration is to some extent inevitable, the ageing process can be delayed by exercise. As we grow older, rapid downhill changes will take place if we do not put up a fight to prevent them.

Tough muscles all over your body represent a safety mechanism for the skeleton and joints like a built-in corset. Strong back muscles will prevent damage to the delicate bones of the spine, they will act as shock absorbers and cushions against injury. A tight, firm stomach will protect the abdominal organs from injury and prolapse, preventing the protruding stomach characteristic of middle age. Often 'middle-age spread' is caused not so much by overweight as by lack of muscular support, and bad posture.

Taut muscles across the upper back will straighten the shoulders and improve posture, which will affect the way in which all the internal organs are aligned. Good posture will not only make you appear taller and more confident, it will pull in your stomach, support your bustline better and immediately make you appear ten years younger.

A good carriage is very important indeed if a bodybuilder has any competitive ambitions. The way in which a woman moves reveals a great deal about her personality and level of self-confidence. The most beautiful women often owe more to their body movements than their features and the ideal to which we should all aspire is undoubtedly the feline grace of the cat. Just watch how it stretches, its incredible flexibility through about 180°, then the sudden spring as all its reserves of energy and razor-sharp reflexes come into play. It also has the ability to relax totally, as if filleted of its bones.

Remedial Weight-Training

Weight-training can be used remedially when serious injuries have been sustained. This type of training should always be carried out under medical supervision and with the help of a knowledgeable and experienced instructor. In time, injured areas can normally be strengthened and their movement restored. One of the recent British champions in women's bodybuilding had a leg almost severed in a car crash and took up weight-training to overcome the continuous pain she suffered. Now she can squat-lift more weight than some men.

BODY TYPES

There are three basic body types, and everyone is a combination of all three, with one of the three dominant. The three types are endomorph; mesomorph and ectomorph.

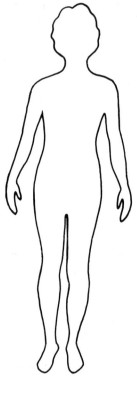

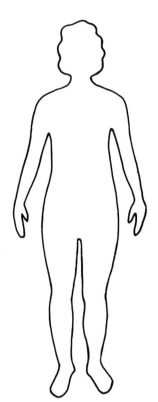

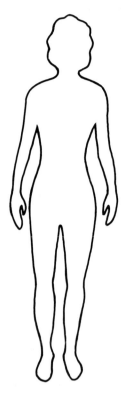

Mesomorph   *Endomorph*   *Ectomorph*

1. *Endomorphs*

This type is normally short in stature, with rounded soft contours. Endomorphs have a high proportion of fat tissue and a low level of muscularity. They have wide hips and a tendency to put on fat around the lower body and stomach. Endomorphs characteristically have a placid disposition, with a natural tendency to conserve effort and therefore energy. Their movements are slow and deliberate and they often avoid exercise and favour sedentary occupations and pastimes. They have a low metabolic rate and their system tends to convert food to fat more readily than the other body types.

Their desire to slim is usually acute, but it is also harder for them than anyone else. Because of their low basal metabolic rate (BMR), they probably eat far less than other slimmer people with different body types and still gain weight so their diet should be calorie-controlled – low in fat and sugars, and relatively high in fruits, vegetables and other complex carbohydrates. For endomorphs, the only answer to weight-loss is regular aerobic exercise – low-level, sustained activities such as jogging, cycling or swimming – combined with a weight-training programme.

As far as weight-training is concerned, endomorphs can benefit in many ways. Weights will build up their muscle tissue, which will burn more calories, even when resting. Their squarish body

and short limbs mean that their centre of gravity is low and leverage good, so endomorphs can usually handle heavy weights well. Regular training will speed up their metabolic rate, burn more calories, gradually reduce bodyfat, and instil the habit of adopting a more energetic approach to life. If endomorphs can overcome their habitual inertia and control their nutrition, then they are often very successful bodybuilders.

2. *Mesomorphs*

Mesomorphs are basically muscular and athletic, with the disadvantage that, if they add fat on top of the muscle, they develop a thick, chunky look, with no waistline, so becoming more endomorphic in appearance. Lazy mesomorphs can therefore become pretty unshapely as they grow older and the extra weight can be difficult to lose.

They tend to require exercise as a necessity of life and become wretched and difficult without it. Fortunately, they also tend to be disciplined and strong-willed and usually force themselves back into action and into shape. Their diet should be moderate in protein, high in complex carbohydrate, low in fat, and they need to watch their calories too. As bodybuilders, they have the most natural advantages to build muscle easily and quickly and in good proportions, and have plenty of energy for intensive work-outs.

3. *Ectomorphs*

Ectomorphs are characterized by poor muscular development. They normally have narrow shoulders, slim hips, and long limbs. They do not usually have a weight problem and seem able to eat anything they want without getting fat, to the disgust of the rest of us. An ectomorph who puts on weight in later life tends to collect it around the waist, giving an unattractive central bulge to a matchstick figure.

From the bodybuilding viewpoint, ectomorphs have the most problems. Their long limbs mean that the muscles are long and thin and, because of the problems of leverage, it is harder for them to handle really heavy weights in order to build muscle size.

The extreme leanness of many ectomorphs requires them to gain a great deal of muscle size in order to see a real improvement, and gaining weight can be much more difficult for them, than losing it can be for an endomorph. This is because many ectomorphs are quick-moving, high-energy people, and they are inclined to have a very fast metabolism which burns off all they eat.

Training for this body type should consist of heavy basic weight exercises, no aerobic activity, and as much rest as possible between work-outs because this will conserve energy and aid muscle-building by keeping the metabolic rate as slow as possible. Their diet should concentrate on many small high-protein, high-carbohydrate snacks at regular intervals through the day, combined with two or three protein-supplement drinks which is the ideal way to eat for muscular weight-gain.

No one is a pure example of one body type. Mine for instance is primarily mesomorph, with a lot of ectomorph, and a little endomorph, and my training and diet have to be angled to take into account these aspects of my physical make-up.

The bodybuilder strives all the time to achieve a more mesomorphic appearance either by reducing endomorphic fat, or building muscle on an ectomorphic frame. You can do a great deal to improve yourself in this way. There is obviously nothing you can do about your bone structure, but you can certainly rearrange everything else.

The potential of the individual to improve is therefore limited to a certain extent by her basic body type, but if training and diet are suitably adapted, then anyone can capitalize on their efforts to the maximum degree. Many books and articles on weight-training do not seem to take this body-type factor into consideration, giving the impression that the same diet and training techniques will have a miraculous effect on everyone who uses them. This is not the case.

I cannot stress enough that each individual must objectively analyse what her own problems and aims are, and then apply the principles outlined in this book in a personal way. As a rank beginner, practically any training you do, or any diet you try, will produce dramatic results for a limited period of time. As you continue training and dieting, improvement will become much slower and you will need continually to assess and refine your techniques to suit your personal physical make-up and metabolism.

MENTAL ATTITUDE

There is no need to accept that the body you have is the one with which you are permanently stuck. If you have the right mental attitude you will say to yourself, 'Hang on a minute; I can do something about it. I won't accept it. I'm going to keep my health, looks and fitness come what may . . .' As you get older you need more and more exercise to combat probable weight gain perhaps due to childbirth and a generally more sedentary existence. Looking after yourself is not vanity, it is your responsibility and insurance policy.

With increasing age, it will be initially harder to get fit and to maintain that fitness. Yet the advantages are enormous, since the quality of your whole life will be improved. A young woman with naturally good muscle-tone may take a much shorter time to get into shape than an overweight older woman who has neglected herself for years. The answer is to take it slowly. If you start gently, and progress steadily, then results will gradually show and they will be more durable. Think young, be prepared to work hard to achieve your aim and give yourself plenty of time. There is no magic formula. What you get out of it depends on what you put in. If you skip work-outs, eat junk food, stay up late and cheat yourself you will not make progress.

Appraise yourself honestly, strip off your clothes and look at yourself critically in the mirror. You almost certainly will not like what you see, but be cool and analytical. Decide whether you want to lose inches from your waist or hips and then, when you have isolated the problem, translate your wishes into willpower to get into the gym and do something about it. It is a good idea to have someone take a photograph of you at the start – a really cruel one, in a bikini or swimsuit. Get an enlarged print, draw around your body the outline which you really desire, then stick the photograph on the door of the refrigerator as a deterrent and inspiration. Look at your original photograph at intervals and check how you are progressing towards your ideal image. The mind is a great motivator and if you want to look that way badly enough then, eventually, you will.

The mental image will translate into a gritty determination to succeed: your body can be changed, and changed beyond recognition if you so will it.

Imagining your ultimate objective is very important indeed. The mind is infinitely stronger than the muscles. It can actually programme them to develop in the way you want. So if you want to lose weight from your thighs and buttocks, or add mass to your upper body, then you need to concentrate your thinking on achieving that goal.

Once you have the right mental attitude, you are ready to begin. You must have a real commitment, know what you want and be prepared to put in maximum effort to achieve it. Start a regular training programme with realistic goals, preferably short-term, and stick to it. Do not let your mind and body cheat you to avoid your work-outs. Don't fool yourself. Once you have overcome your initial inertia, then each battle you win with your baser instincts will be a triumph. You can learn to look at a cake and not eat it in order to achieve a super body – and you can learn to get in the gym and work-out rather than go home and watch TV and nibble all evening. Once you start to discipline your body, you will begin to feel confidence in other areas of your life as well. Believe in your progress and it will happen.

Chapter Two

HOW TO START

The hardest part of any exercise programme is the beginning. You will never make a more difficult move or lift a heavier weight than getting your bottom off your armchair, into a leotard or shorts, ready to begin. If you imagine that anyone finds it easy to give up the evening 'pleasures' of a drink, long meal and relaxation in front of the television, in favour of a two-hour work-out in the gym and a fish salad afterwards, you are mistaken. At any level, regular exercise requires self-discipline – no one has ever said it was easy. Your greatest enemy is yourself, and your greatest battle is with your mind.

There is no excuse for not having time to exercise. Some of the busiest, most successful people in the world fit regular exercise into their lives and benefit from it in increased energy, stamina and mental alertness. So skip a lunch one day and join a keep-fit class, or go for a swim – but stop thinking that exercise is something to be fitted into a busy life. Exercise is as essential as eating and sleeping. It is something around which other activities must be arranged, and a fundamental, necessary part of your life.

One word of warning – regular exercise, like dieting, is unfortunately regarded, in this country, as a mild eccentricity. It is acceptable to play golf or squash occasionally, even to swim or jog a little, but once you admit to lifting weights you are definitely 'odd'. From the very start of my own interest in exercise, beginning with keep-fit and progressing to competitive bodybuilding, I have encountered an increasing amount of negativism, ridicule, scepticism and sheer bloody-minded antagonism. Most of it has been provoked by ignorance, chauvinism and envy. On the other hand, many people have been fascinated, intrigued and sufficiently impressed by the results achieved to try it for themselves. So do not be put off by what anyone else thinks of you.

If you begin to exercise at home and encounter negative remarks, then choose a room in which you can be alone, or a time of day when you are unlikely to be interrupted. Make sure it is understood that your exercise session is sacrosanct, that nobody is allowed to intrude and that you are in deadly earnest. Once you begin to feel the benefits, do not bother to defend your new interest or to convert anyone else to your way of life. There is a tremendous temptation to become an evangelist for exercise and diet – and at the same time an incredible bore. Let the results speak for themselves in your new shape and glow of good health – no one can ignore those!

Having psyched yourself into starting, the next step is to decide exactly how to go about it. The first thing to consider is what you wish to achieve. If you want to lose weight, then a type of exercise which burns fat would be best, for instance, cycling, swimming, jogging, or an aerobic dance class. If you wish to become generally fitter, stronger and more flexible, keep-fit, yoga or circuit weight-training should be your aim. If you want to achieve your maximum potential by reshaping your body completely, then bodybuilding, or at least a regular weight-training session, will be most beneficial. Whatever you choose you will have to start gently. If you are over thirty, or have not exercised at all for years, or if you take any type of drug regularly or smoke heavily, it is advisable to have a check-up with your doctor before starting any type of exercise programme and to give up smoking anyway. One girl of twenty came to a keep-fit class of mine, did thirty seconds of spot-jogging and passed out – a combination of unfitness and lack of breakfast – so you must take care of yourself.

It is a great mistake to expect your body to cope with too much, too soon. Every muscle and tendon will fight back at the start, and you will ache so much you will wish you had stayed at home after all. You must condition your bodily systems to accept the extra new stress and workload. So, however enthusiastic you are, or however fit you think you are, moderation is the safest course. You should start to see a noticeable improvement in appearance within six weeks, and in three months can expect to achieve good all-round fitness with consistent effort.

Initially, the ideal amount of exercise you take should be a half-hour session three times each week (say on Monday/Wednesday/Friday or Tuesday/Thursday/Saturday), with one complete day's rest in between to recover. Once you have reached a state of general fitness, it is actually easier to sustain the condition than to achieve it in the first place, but you must be consistent. Fitness is easily lost and within three months of not exercising you could lose all you have gained and be back to square one. As far as muscle is concerned, the hardest part is building muscle bulk, but once you have done it, it is there for good. If training ceases, the muscles may become smaller but the mind retains a kind of 'muscle memory' of what previously existed, and a short period of training will soon restore your former condition.

BASIC EQUIPMENT

Free Weights

If you are starting from scratch, you can use a couple of tins or empty washing-up liquid containers filled with sand or water, but you will soon progress beyond such a rudimentary stage. Most sports shops and chain stores these days stock basic weight-training equipment and there are also many advertisements in magazines selling weights by mail order or second-hand in local papers. If you start by training at home, you will need to buy a barbell with adjustable plates and a set of dumb-bells as the basic requirements. These are generally termed 'free weights' (as opposed to 'machine weights' such as Nautilus and multigym equipment). Once you have them they will last for ever.

The *barbell* is the basic piece of equipment for weight-training. It is usually four, five or six feet long and made of steel. It consists of a bar, sleeve, collars and plates. The basic bar, without plates, normally weighs 5 lbs per foot and the more expensive ones are equipped with a hollow metal *sleeve* which encases the centre of the bar, and allows it to revolve in use. This can be a help when doing certain exercises.

The bar, or its collar, will have crisscross grooves or '*knurling*' cut into it to prevent you losing your grip when your hands perspire.

Plates are flat discs which range in size from 1¼ lbs to about 100 lbs. Some are marked in pounds, some in kilos (2.2 lbs). They have a hole in the middle and can be fixed in different weight combinations on to the basic barbell.

Plates can be made of steel or vinyl-covered

concrete. The latter are easier on carpets at home and not as noisy to use, but they are also much more bulky. It is easier to increase the number of plates on a bar if they are made of slim metal. Inside and outside the plates are metal clamps called *collars* which hold the plates in position on the bar. The outer collar will have some kind of locking device to hold it in place, some of which require a separate '*key*' to unlock. Other types have spring clips. Never lift a bar without collars fixed firmly in position, or the plates could slide off one end unexpectedly and cause injury or accident.

A wide range of barbells and plates should be provided in a gym and should be stored on racks in order of weight. Sometimes, if the gym is particularly well-equipped and can supply a sufficiently large amount of bars in a wide range of weights, the barbells and dumb-bells will have the plates soldered on to them. This saves a lot of time when training as you do not have to stop to change the plates.

The *Olympic barbell* is a specialized type used in weight-lifting contests and heavy bodybuilding training, the basic bar weighing 20 kilos, and each collar weighing 2½ kilos. Olympic bars are wider and longer than the regular kind and are very useful for performing heavy exercises such as the squat, deadlift and benchpress.

Basic free weight equipment

Dumb-bells are, in effect, very short barbells for use in one hand and are normally used in pairs. These also come in either adjustable or non-adjustable form. For home use the adjustable type are preferable, so you only need to have one set, plus a variety of plates. In the gym, non-adjustable fixed weights are much quicker and safer to use, particularly for overhead exercises or for those where the dumb-bells are held over the face at any point.

Other equipment for home use can include a *narrow bench* with two supporting struts at one end. This can be used for the bench press, or any other exercise requiring you to lie down. If you buy the type with an adjustable top which will prop upright, then it will enable you to do a much wider range of shoulder and arm exercises. Most gyms are equipped with simple benches for abdominal work and also a few of the more complex kind for multi-exercise work.

For home use, have an old *broomstick* handy for doing waist twists. *Ankle/wrist weights*, which tie on, can be obtained from most sports shops and are very useful for performing arm or leg exercises with extra resistance.

For the beginner, the first sight of a good gymnasium is reminiscent of a medieval torture chamber and is completely bewildering. It can be most offputting if you have to ask what everything is for and how to use it. The basic equipment to look for in a good gym should consist of the following: first and foremost a good range of barbells and dumb-bells – look for plenty of fairly light ones if you are a beginner. There is no point in joining the type of gym where the dumb-bells start at 35 lbs weight because you will need some of 3 to 5 lbs and barbells of 10, 15, 20 lbs. Make sure they rise in weight in easy stages, and also make sure they don't stop at 50 lbs because you will get stronger very quickly, and may soon be squatting 100 lbs or more.

Machine Weights

There is a very wide range of machines available, but the most important are the combined leg extension and leg curl machine; the lat. pulldown machine (which can be used for a wide range of exercises with a bar and also for cable work); squat-racks, leg-press and hack-squat machines. In a well-equipped gym, there should be a variety of wallbars to support abdominal boards at different angles, a benchpress rack, horizontal chinning bar, parallel bars and plenty of benches. Most of these machines are illustrated in Chapter 4.

Multigym machines have become very popular in leisure centres, YMCAs, schools, and so on, because they provide facilities for several individuals to train at once and also take up far less space than racks of free weights. The main drawback of such machines is that each exercise station offers movement in only one limited range, whereas free weights can be used to hit a muscle from hundreds of different angles. In a busy gym, multigyms are in constant use and it is maddening to have to queue up to use one. They are useful in combination with free weight training for light fitness or toning, but for bodybuilders to train exclusively on them would be inadvisable since they can encourage the belief that the machine is doing all the work, and less effort tends to be expended than when working with free weights. They are useful for beginners since they cut out the need for a spotter (training partner) and remove the elements of skill and coordination required to handle free weights.

The latest arrivals on the exercise scene in Britain are **Nautilus machines**. They have been in widespread use in the USA for nearly twenty years and have been extensively tried and tested. Each machine is designed to exercise an individual body part or muscle under continuously applied stress and throughout its full range of movement, which is something that free weights cannot do.

Nautilus can be very effective in making rapid strength gains and fun to use for a change. However, they do have some drawbacks. Because the equipment is expensive and needs a qualified Nautilus instructor to teach you the system, most Nautilus gyms have high membership fees. The machines share the same problem as the multigym in that they exercise only one muscle or muscle group throughout one range of movement, and only a limited number of exercises are possible compared with free weights. Because the Nautilus system is promoted as a means of providing a total body work-out, gyms using Nautilus often do not have a range of free weights as well. The Nautilus system claims to keep you in incredible shape if it is used for three twenty-minute sessions each week. In a busy gym, at peak hours, the machines have to be used on a circuit-training basis to push a lot of people through the system in a short time. This is frustrating if you want to do some strenuous and repetitive exercises and also to take your time. However, there are plenty of good bodybuilders who swear by Nautilus and make good progress, so try them out for yourself.

On the whole, I think beginners should concentrate on learning the considerable skill of handling free weights. It isn't easy, because you need to learn coordination, balance, correct breathing technique and confidence, as well as the technicalities of the various exercises, correct form and safety principles. Once these basics are mastered, the variety of exercises you can perform with a very limited amount of equipment is endless. If you are on holiday abroad, or away from home, or outside a big city, you will not find it easy to train if you know only how to use sophisticated machines. You are unlikely to have difficulty finding somewhere which has a rudimentary free weight training facility.

If you are lucky enough to belong to a gym which has free weights, Nautilus and multigym facilities, then you have an ideal combination. Substitute Nautilus for some of your free weight exercises, or supplement your work-out with specific Nautilus isolation exercises (e.g. the leg adductor and leg abductor), which are hard to do with free weights. Advanced bodybuilders should start to use a combination of free weights and machines as soon as possible but always remember that however technologically advanced the machine, you still have to work really hard to make progress.

CHOOSING A GYM

It can be very demoralizing to join a club and find yourself surrounded by experienced weight-trainers who seem to know precisely what they are doing, only to find that the instructor gives you a body-conditioning fitness programme which does not allow you to use weights for several weeks.

For this reason, I would recommend that if you are really unfit or overweight, you begin by doing the basic groundwork in private at home, or at least, in a gentle keep-fit class where nobody knows you! In Chapter 4 I have included a series of exercises which are suitable for complete beginners. When you can carry out these exercises with ease, and your fitness level and morale have both risen a little then you will be ready to think about joining a club to start weight-training.

After this preliminary start at home it is essential to have some proper qualified instruction in weight-training before you go any further, and this is most easily obtained by membership of a reputable club.

There are two prime reasons for joining a gym, other than the obvious social advantages. First and foremost: safety. In a well-run gym newcomers should be given instruction in safe handling of weights and gym discipline before they embark on any training at all. Weight-training must be progressive to be effective. The muscles will not become stronger and grow unless they are consistently overloaded with more and more weight and a good gym will ensure that these principles are applied to help you maintain progress. Because heavy weights are involved, (and 'heavy' does not necessarily mean hundreds of pounds but merely the amount required by the individual to overload a muscle group), safety becomes a critical factor. It is downright dangerous to do some exercises (for example the bench press, or heavy squats), without someone else watching to ensure that you are not pinned underneath an immovable weight because of an accident. Fatal accidents have occurred as the result of over-confident solitary training.

The second reason for joining a good gym is to learn the proper techniques for lifting weights and how to perform an exercise in 'strict form'. This can make all the difference between success and failure in a bodybuilding programme. When you are taught a new exercise you should always be told, or ask, exactly how it should be performed, and precisely which muscles or muscle-group the exercise affects. There is no excuse for performing an exercise with your body and not using your brain at the same time. Right from the word 'go' it is essential to perform your exercises correctly and invariably that will mean in the most difficult way, probably using less weight. If you get into bad habits at the start, they will just get worse and worse until they are almost impossible to eradicate, and then you are a danger to yourself and to others. If you can handle a 5-kilo weight properly, then later on you will be able to use 50 kilos without injuring yourself.

Handling free weights is not easy. You need to learn how to perform a wide range of exercises in the correct way, with correct breathing and style. There is no surer sign of a bad weight-trainer than a lot of grunts and groans and weights being crashed on to the floor. The most successful bodybuilders, those with the very best physiques, are usually working quietly, with concentration, in a corner alone.

Having decided that you would like to join a gym or club, you will encounter one of the main problems facing a potential female bodybuilder in this country today. The sport is so new, that most gyms either have not heard of it or do not know how to teach it to women. If we were discussing training in North America you would be able to find facilities and instruction widely available, but Britain is another matter. One or two beginners' weight-training courses are starting up, and I am certain that there will be many more in the near future. Meanwhile, watch out for ads or ask at your YMCA, Leisure Centre or local club about courses – they may decide to start one if there is sufficient demand.

There is a great division between what can be broadly termed a 'health club' and a proper working gymnasium. Plenty of health clubs are springing up offering facilities such as sauna, jacuzzi, facials, health-food bars, massage, slimming treatments, and so on, together with limited facilities for weight-training and exercise. Most clubs of this kind concentrate on combining a very light exercise programme (perhaps 30 to 60 minutes of stretching, callisthenics, aerobics or general keep-fit), with a

A typical gym.

dietary régime designed primarily for the overweight woman. My advice to an aspiring bodybuilder, however, is to steer well clear of such health clubs since they do not always have staff qualified or experienced in weight-training and many actively discourage bodybuilding for women. I have heard of more than one instance where a bodybuilder has been pressurized to leave a club because the other women members were put off by the sight of hard work – and that was bad for business.

So, where can you train? At present there is no comprehensive list available of really well-equipped gyms, with good instruction and pleasant, clean, well-organized surroundings. The English Federation of Bodybuilders can provide details of a limited number of approved gyms throughout the country but, on the whole, you will simply have to look around and find one that suits you. The principal criterion is to find somewhere conveniently close to where you work or live. There is no point in joining a club which takes you more than half an hour to reach. The willpower to drag yourself there at the end of a tiring day is a pretty fragile commodity and if you face a long cold walk, a crowded journey on public transport, or a tiresome drive, then you are going to start skipping work-outs unless you have the dedication of a superwoman. Most people start out experimentally and can be easily deterred, so try to reduce the factors which will sap your willpower. Make it easy and attractive to train and then you will stick to it. I would also advise joining for only three to six months at first, until you are sure weight-training is for you and that the surroundings of the club are congenial.

A well-run gym should be spacious and well-ventilated. The floor should be uncluttered and weights should be kept neatly in their racks when not in use. The gym floor should have a good non-slip surface (not a tatty old scuffed carpet). There should be a businesslike atmosphere of people training, not sitting on equipment chatting and definitely not fooling around. Look for other serious bodybuilders working-out because you can learn a great deal by asking them questions, as well as using them as a source of inspiration. Make sure there are qualified, experienced, knowledgeable and interested instructors on hand at all times who can provide you with an individually tailored programme suitable for your needs and keep an eye on your progress. Ask a lot of pertinent questions and make sure that you join somewhere which will provide the right facilities for you. Be sure to tell the instructor about any past injuries, weaknesses or health problems you may have, before you start.

If you are in need of instruction and lack experience, avoid joining the type of club where the equipment is superb and the supervision non-existent. If you can train at offpeak times, during the day, you will probably get more personal attention from the instructor than if you go along during peak hours, after work, when the gym will be very crowded. At such times you will have to hang around waiting for equipment and will get cold and discouraged.

Do not automatically rule out an all-male gym. Any girl bodybuilding in this country today is in a pioneering position and, as in other previously exclusive male areas, we have to start somewhere. Once one girl joins a gym, others soon follow and the process will accelerate all over the country. Bodybuilding for women is the sport of the 1980s, and any gym worthy of its name will have to adapt to women members or die!

If you feel intimidated by training in an all-male gym then take heart because most serious weight-trainers are very friendly people, bound up in their common interest and only too glad to help out with advice and practical assistance. They may look askance at the first female intrusion into their hallowed domain but once they get used to you training regularly, hard and seriously and not chatting or distracting them, then you will be accepted and, rather unflatteringly, become 'one of the boys'. They will probably also watch your safety when you are using heavy weights and give friendly advice.

You will probably find that you try several places for short periods before you discover somewhere really congenial. Some people like to belong to two or even three different places so that they can have a change of scene occasionally. I like to train somewhere different for a short period before a competition, just for extra stimulus when the training becomes tough, and where people leave me alone when I get dishevelled, hot and tired!

CLOTHES AND PERSONAL EQUIPMENT FOR THE GYM

Weight-training is not a fashion show, so do not spend an hour dressing for the experience. Weights and equipment are often rusty and covered with grease and some exercises, like abdominal crunches, have to be performed lying on a none-too-clean gym floor. It is important to keep warm so that the muscles are flexible and you avoid injuries. On the other hand, there is nothing to be gained by becoming too hot. Any weight lost through sweating will be replaced by the first drink you take and wearing 'sweatsuits' can cause the body to become dangerously overheated, so that you will only feel exhausted and enervated instead of strong and energetic. The best kit to choose is leotard and shorts or tee-shirt and tracksuit trousers. Your main concern should be comfort and unrestricted movement.

Your outfit should be flexible, absorbent and warm, especially if the weather is cold and your muscles are stiff. I prefer to have bare arms and legs most of the year, so that I can see the muscles working and observe whether they are responding properly to an exercise but other girls prefer to remain covered up. There is something to be said for wearing a flattering outfit which will give you a good self-image, raise your morale, and encourage you to work harder. Have two or three sets of clothing if you train regularly, since there never seems to be time in the week to wash everything repeatedly and you will not be nice to know if you wear your kit more than once.

If you are overweight and self-conscious, try a black leotard and tights but avoid wearing baggy clothing which allows you to hide your shape completely. You want to remain aware of your shortcomings, not conceal them.

Absolutely essential equipment is a good pair of training shoes with ridged soles, together with thick socks. When lifting heavy weights it is of prime importance not to slip or lose your balance at a critical moment.

If you have long hair or a fringe, an elasticated headband is a good idea. Long hair can be tucked up into it, so that it does not get caught up during exercises involving the shoulders and, of course, if you get very hot, it will prevent sweat running into your eyes. Absorbent wristbands are helpful, so that you can mop your fevered brow, and a small towel is also useful since some exercises (such as the squat) require padding around the bar to make it more comfortable.

Most bodybuilders wear a wide leather weight-lifter's belt, although they are not strictly necessary unless you are doing very heavy overhead lifting. They give a feeling of confidence by supporting the midsection and can encourage the user to put more effort into heavy exercise such as the squat or deadlift. The idea of these exercises is, among other benefits, to strengthen the lower back muscles, so the wearing of an aid to support the back and stomach artificially actually inhibits the strengthening process. Bodybuilders ought not to lift such heavy weights that a belt becomes essential. I tend to wear my belt regularly due to an old back injury.

One aspect of bodybuilding for women which is definitely not advantageous, is that you will develop hands like a workman. Habitually lifting heavy metal bars produces a double row of calluses on the palms of the hands below each finger. No one seems to have overcome this problem as yet but the use of gymnasts' grips seems to help a little. These are suede thongs which fit around the middle fingers, extend across the palm of the hand and fasten around the wrists. They have an important function in ensuring a secure grip on the barbells and other equipment when your hands get sweaty, but still do not seem entirely to inhibit the development of the unsightly corns. Weight-lifters' gloves, with padded palms and cut-off fingers, are the best aid. These can be obtained from American muscle magazines by mail order and some sports shops sell their own brand. Cycling-mitts can also be used.

Ankle-weights can be obtained from most sports shops and used for adding extra weight when performing abdominal exercises such as leg-raises. They are very useful for home use but not very practical if you have to carry lead weights to the gym in your kitbag every day.

If you perform heavy squats or deadlifts, it can be helpful to wrap the knees with wide crêpe bandages. This will not be necessary for most women bodybuilders as the weight used will never be great enough to require the extra support.

WHEN TO TRAIN

The part of the day that you choose to train depends on personal preference and the time you have available. There is really no best moment and some famous bodybuilders even train in the middle of the night. Ideally, you should try to train when your blood sugar level is at its highest. You will have to find out for yourself when that is: it may be thirty minutes, or two hours after you eat, depending on the content of your pre-exercise meal. One thing is certain, if you starve all day, and then work-out, you will flake out. Try to eat a small quantity of some complex carbohydrate an hour or so prior to your work-out for energy, and protein afterwards to help

the tissues to recover.

Once you have decided on a regular time to train, try to stick to it. The body thrives on routine and will conserve its resources to deal with the overload it anticipates during your work-out. So try not to upset your metabolism by erratic training hours. I generally train between six P.M. and eight P.M. when I've had two meals, and three hours at least have elapsed since the last one.

If I train at lunchtime, as happens occasionally, then it always seems far more of an effort because my body is not used to it and rebels. Equally, if I eat a decent lunch with a glass of wine, I might as well forget the work-out later! If you feel sluggish and enervated, wanting only to skip your work-out and go home, then this is the time you must go to the gym. Exercise is what you need, not rest, to make you feel better. A work-out will revive you, fill you with new energy and give your spirits a lift.

HOW OFTEN AND HOW LONG TO TRAIN

Beginners should not initially train for longer than 20 to 30 minutes, three times per week, with a day's rest in between. This should gradually build up to 1 hour.

Intermediates need around 1 hour four times a week, training on a split routine (see pp. 92–94), e.g. Monday/Tuesday: Thursday/Friday, with Wednesday/Saturday/Sunday to rest.

Advanced trainers can intensify work-outs to train five or six days each week (see Advanced Split Schedules, pp. 107–112). Split work-outs are designed to allow each muscle group sufficient recovery time. Work-outs should last no longer than 1½ hours each session. Even top competitors train no longer than this, but instead introduce intensifying techniques (see pp. 100–105).

If you habitually train longer than this, you are either not working hard enough or you are overtraining. The only exception would be prior to a contest when for the final six to eight weeks work-outs need to be longer, perhaps 2 hours in all, but weights will necessarily be lighter and rest intervals shorter (see pp. 108–112).

WHEN NOT TO TRAIN

If you are ill or injured, do not train at all, but of course if you are just a little 'under the weather' or suffering a mild strain you may actually feel better for a work-out. There are dozens of occasions when I have crawled to the gym feeling terrible, and emerged later feeling on top of the world. If you have a bad cold or a virus, give up, go home and have an early night. If you have been ill and have missed a week or more of training, ease gradually back into your programme. Do not be over-enthusiastic and overdo it at once. You will have lost strength and stamina and it will take a few work-outs to return to your previous level. Three days without any exercise is a long time for the body.

Do not train until about two hours after a meal because the process of digestion concentrates blood in the stomach and makes it very difficult to place demands on the muscles as well. It will also make you feel uncomfortable inside.

If you are unable to concentrate properly due to personal problems or are very upset, then it is a good idea to call it a day – lack of concentration means accidents and injuries and as far as building the muscles is concerned, you will be wasting your time. Controlled anger or stress channelled into aggression, on the other hand, may give you a great work-out!

TRAINING DIARY

One all-important piece of personal equipment in the gym will be your training diary. You can either use a notebook or daily diary, or buy a special bodybuilders' notebook (available from specialist shops or large booksellers, or by mail order from muscle magazines). In this you should write down the details of every work-out you do. Note down the exercises, how many times you manage to perform them and how much weight you use. Record your mood and feelings, whether you feel listless and tired, or energetic and high. Note the time of day you exercised and how long the work-out lasted.

Make detailed notes on your food intake for the day, and how you reacted to it. Some foods will make you feel sluggish, others will energize you – learn to recognize which they are (see section on 'Individualizing your Diet', p. 116 and Allergies, p. 117). You should note your weight at intervals, no more than once a week, on the same day, but do not be a slave to the scales, concern yourself rather with your appearance in the mirror. If you begin to like what you see then you are obviously doing the right thing, so stick to it.

You can also periodically make a note of your overall body dimensions – about once a month. In addition to the usual statistics, add your upper arm, forearm, thigh, calf and chest measurements. If your club has facilities for carrying out a bodyfat percentage test, using calipers, then add that information as well: it will be very useful if you compete. Some of the better-equipped new gyms in

London and elsewhere have complete fitness-testing facilities and you can have a periodic check to ensure that your development is progressing. If it is not, change your programme or your diet, or both.

You should also have photographs taken of yourself at regular intervals to monitor your progress. You can paste these in your training diary too. The camera is depressingly honest, and you will soon see the areas you need to improve, which your reflection in the mirror will not always reveal. It is human nature to admire your own big biceps and ignore your wobbly backside.

SLEEP, REST AND RELAXATION

Apart from working-out regularly and eating correctly, there is a third essential factor in achieving complete fitness – rest. Without a correct balance between all three elements, success will be elusive.

On the days in between work-outs, it is essential to rest so the muscles can recover, strengthen, grow and prepare their reserves for the next onslaught. As your body grows accustomed to working-out, it will learn to recover more rapidly, aided by proper nutrition. At first, apart from localized muscular soreness, you may experience an overall feeling of real tiredness until your general fitness and stamina improve. This is a sign that you should rest until your batteries are recharged.

On days when you are not working-out in the gym, you can relax by going for a jog or a swim. 'Rest' does not necessarily mean total collapse. Active relaxation is much better for your body, especially if you are concerned about weight-loss, or maintaining your bodyfat at a low level. The only exception should be if you are underweight, and trying to make gains, in which case you should take as little aerobic exercise as possible and rest as much as you can, to keep your metabolic rate slow and conserve energy.

As you become more advanced, you will progress to a four-days-a-week programme, working upper and lower body twice each week. Rest is essential between training sessions in order to build muscle. As you work-out, you put your muscles and every bodily system under great strain, in particular, the endocrine system which needs to adapt to your new régime and keep pace with the extra demands being made on your system. This adaptation actually takes longer than muscular gain. On your day off, every system has a chance to recover. If you keep on exercising, you will not progress but will merely become chronically tired. The days of rest are almost more important to your progress than the training sessions! How much sleep you need will depend on your own requirements. You may find four hours enough – or you may need ten. If you feel half-dead all the time, get more rest and sleep.

ACHES, PAINS AND INJURIES

Injuries and strains should not occur at all if you make sure you warm-up properly before you start, you do not stop for a chat and cool down in the middle of a session and then return to lift a heavy weight, and, finally, if you stretch. Always lift in the correct way. Do not lift too much too soon, do not lift when you are overtired and do not lift to show off.

The aches experienced after a normal work-out are a sign that you worked hard and effectively and you should welcome them. As you become generally fitter, stronger and more flexible, you will encounter aches and pains less frequently, unless you employ an unfamiliar exercise in your regular programme. These aches are caused by the build-up of toxic substances, especially lactic acid, in the muscles during exercise. The body produces a natural painkiller which will mask muscular aches for about twenty-four hours, so if you work-out in the early evening, you will probably feel stiff by teatime next day. During your rest day, the bloodstream will gradually disperse toxins. If you ache a great deal, or experience undue stiffness, then stretch or perform a few keep-fit exercises. This will improve bloodflow to the area and carry away the waste products more easily.

If you experience any discomfort or pain when trying an exercise for the first time, stop doing it immediately. There are hundreds of variations and you can always work round a weakness. Bear in mind that a little discomfort may be good for you. For instance, a weakness in your ankle from an old sprain will be strengthened by weight-training. Weights are, after all, used for remedial training in some hospitals in order to help patients recover from serious injuries and illnesses.

Be especially careful of your back at all times, and always lift and put down weights properly – in everyday life, as well as in the gym. (See pp. 42–43 for a description and illustration of how to do this correctly.) Obviously, a short, sharp pain or one that persists is a sign that you are injured. In an emergency, apply ice cubes immediately to a muscle injury and where possible strap it and rest the injured part in an elevated position. This will cause the blood vessels to constrict, inhibit bleeding and reduce the amount of fluid transported to the injury area, thereby reducing swelling and bruising. Be inventive in an emergency. I once clutched a frozen salmon all the way home to help an injured arm. Consult a doctor or osteopath as soon as possible.

If treatment is given in the first twenty-four hours, even quite a nasty tear can be quickly alleviated. Do not take painkillers to mask the discomfort because they will prevent you from knowing where the injury is located and may cause you to injure the area further. Let the body tell you what it can or cannot do while the injury persists and keep the injury mobile by gentle stretching, unless it is really serious, as this will discourage fluid retention and bruising and the build-up of toxins which cause pain. To heal quickly, the area needs a better blood supply, not a worse one. Training can continue if you work around the injury and do not attempt any exercise which hurts you but if you really cannot work in the gym, try swimming instead. I found this beneficial when I could barely walk from back pain, after an injury.

If you have had any serious health problems, operations, broken limbs, joint problems or dietary imbalances, then make sure that you discuss these with your doctor and your instructor before you embark on any fitness programme. If you have had a serious eating disorder like anorexia nervosa, then any change in your nutrition should be conducted under close medical supervision. Should your doctor or instructor take no interest in your problems, change to someone else. Your instructor should make sure your work-out programme takes into consideration all aspects of your age, condition, weight, fitness level, health and aspirations. If you do not get this personal attention, go to another gym where you do.

I have trained with one arm in a sling, a badly-sprained ankle and a head cold (not all at once) before now – all extremely inadvisable, but it is really amazing what it takes to keep a keen bodybuilder down!

SPECIAL FEMALE CONSIDERATIONS

Physically fit and active women normally do not experience problems with pre-menstrual tension and cramps. Exercise relieves stress and increases bloodflow to the relevant areas. There is certainly no reason to stop weight-training or any other exercise in these circumstances because it will actually help bring relief. Taking a supplement of vitamin B^6 may also do some good.

A very fit bodybuilder may experience a cessation of menstruation altogether, or *amenorrhoea*. This appears to be linked to high-intensity training and low bodyfat levels. Once the bodyfat level is below about ten percent, this condition can occur. The body obviously cannot sustain a pregnancy at such a low level of fat storage, so it reacts accordingly, by making it impossible. Once bodyfat is allowed to rise, the periods will probably return. This condition does no apparent harm to the body and is experienced by many top runners and ballet dancers as well as bodybuilders. It does not indicate you are anorexic, just that you are lean and super fit, and is also very convenient when you are training hard and competing. There is no evidence that ovulation ceases, so do not assume that if you have this condition, you do not need birth control.

As far as birth control is concerned, serious competitors would be better off not taking the Pill from a bodybuilding point of view. The artificial hormone progesterone inhibits the metabolism of protein and reduces muscle mass while encouraging fat deposition, bad news for any bodybuilder! The combined Pill can cause water retention and wreck your attempt to achieve contest definition. However, you will undoubtedly have a worse shape if you are pregnant, so the choice is up to you.

Weight-training can be carried on in suitably modified forms right through a normal pregnancy and afterwards although you should not actually start weight-training at this stage if you have never done it before. The disciplined diet and training routine of bodybuilding should help you to avoid complications and make the whole procedure easier. Women were meant to be physically active during pregnancy, not to sit around as if they might break. If you let yourself go for a year or more, using it as an excuse to overeat, it will take you an agonizingly long hard struggle to get back in shape. If you keep training before and after pregnancy, you will soon be back to normal. Some top competitors have given birth and been back on stage with sharp abdominal definition within a year, so it can be done and need not be feared.

TEN TIPS FOR THE BEGINNER

1 If you are over thirty, overweight or very unfit at any age, have a physical check-up first with your doctor.

2 Tell your instructor at the gym about any medical problems or old injuries you may have.

3 Set small goals at first and progress slowly.

4 If you have a great deal of weight to lose, aim for a gradual loss of 1–2 lbs maximum each week.

5 Work within your limitations and with only your own progress in mind.

6 Have photos taken of yourself in a bikini at the start, and then at regular intervals to record how you progress.

7 Keep a detailed diary to record your training and diet.

8 Revise your diet to a low-fat régime.

9 Make training a habit as essential to your life as eating and sleeping.

10 Never give up!

Chapter Three

BASIC PRINCIPLES OF WEIGHT-TRAINING

PROGRESSIVE OVERLOAD AND MUSCLE GROWTH

'Weight-training' is a generic term which covers all forms of resistance training, either for exercise or competition. Bodybuilding is only one specific application of weight-training among many others and is based on the principle of progressive overload – the capacity of the mind and the body in combination to deal with increased resistance in order to produce muscular and physiological adaptation. This overload is applied in specific ways to work the entire body, to encourage proportional development of a symmetrical and aesthetically pleasing kind. The scientific word for the process by which a muscle grows in size and mass when stressed by an ever increasing workload is *hypertrophy*. This process is optimized by a suitable diet and adequate rest. In stressing the muscles, you unavoidably stress all the other bodily systems. This is only tolerable if it is imposed gradually. If you go too fast, too soon, you will just cause a complete breakdown.

DIFFERENCES IN GROWTH FACTORS AFFECTING MEN AND WOMEN

When training begins, most people have relatively weak muscles, of which some muscle groups will be naturally stronger than others. The legs, for most women, are usually their strongest point but the upper parts of their body, especially the arms and shoulders, are generally weak. Men, on the other hand, have around thirty percent more upper body muscle than women. No one really knows whether this is entirely genetic or due to differences in social behaviour in the way that men and women view and use exercise in adult life, but it is probably a mixture of both. It is a fact that if a man and woman start to train together as beginners and work-out for six months regularly, they will each achieve a similar strength improvement, but the man will develop much larger, more showy muscles. This is because men have a much higher level of the male hormone testosterone in their bodies, which enables them to build muscle far more readily than women. On the other hand, women tend to have a higher pain threshold and better endurance than men, so in a long, high-intensity work-out, women can more than hold their own against men every time. Body for body, women can actually train harder than men!

Muscles on a female physique tend to look more spectacular than on a man, because they are so much more unusual, but muscles on a woman can be beautiful and sexy – starting with the Venus de Milo.

HOW MUSCLES REACT TO OVERLOAD TRAINING

Muscles consist of bundles of long, stringy fibres and when we lift anything a limited number of these are used. Muscle action is a function of the central nervous system and messages are sent by the brain, by means of nerve impulses, to stimulate the muscle fibres to contract. In the course of everyday life the brain will only activate the minimum number of fibres required to cope with any given load. As most people with a sedentary lifestyle experience little physical exertion, the majority of their muscle fibres will never be called into play and so their muscles stay small, weak and flabby through under-exertion.

Once you start to train with weights, a number of interesting things happen. The brain reacts to the extra workload by sending a message to the relevant muscle to bring additional fibres into play. At first, you will notice a few aches and pains as the weak, under-used fibres creak into unaccustomed action. After a while, with continued exercise you will cease to experience this initial discomfort and will notice that lifting has become easier as the extra fibres are used regularly and strengthen. Should you continue training without increasing the workload, you would maintain this new strength level but make no further progress. Weight-training exercise programmes are therefore designed to overload the muscles with progressively heavier weights so that the brain will activate ever more muscle fibres. Continued use of this principle will bring about more and more adaptation until, in theory at least, one hundred percent of your muscular strength capacity is being employed, and the whole of the muscle becomes taut and trim as a result.

It used to be thought that the fibres actually split and increased in number when subjected to this type of training but this is no longer regarded as generally true. It may occur under extreme stress in a few rare cases, but in the vast majority, hypertrophy is a result of the thickening of existing fibres.

However, there is a direct relationship between the amount of weight lifted and the strength, and therefore size, of the muscle lifting it. Since the size of a muscle at its central point is directly proportionate to its length, there is a physical limit to the weight you can lift. Therefore, if you have long limbs and long muscles, you will have to gain a great deal of muscle bulk before it really shows, compared with someone who has a more compact physique, with shorter muscles, where a similar amount of growth will be more obvious. This is why there are very few really tall champion bodybuilders. Most of the world class men probably average around 5 feet 8 in to 5 feet 10 in. However, for those few who work hard enough to build muscle on to a tall thin frame, the end result is really something special. Rare examples are Arnold Schwarzenneger, Lou Ferrigno, Lynne Pirie and Carolyn Cheshire – all top bodybuilding champions with muscularity and height in combination.

HOW TO TRAIN WITH PROGRESSIVE RESISTANCE

The amount of weight required to stimulate muscle strengthening and growth is a very individual matter. Bodybuilding is not weight-lifting, where the lifter seeks to lift the maximum amount possible once only. Your muscles do not know whether they are lifting 40 lbs, 60 lbs, or 100 lbs so there is no point in performing prodigious feats of strength, always striving for maximum poundages. You need just enough weight to overload the muscle working

to capacity, and no more. In general, therefore, use as much weight as you can handle, for the required number of reps (see glossary) specified in your schedule. As soon as you begin to lift a particular weight with relative ease, add extra poundage.

What To Do

Warm-up with a light weight for the first set (see glossary). The weight you use should normally allow you to perform the lowest number of reps recommended in your schedule – the last two of which should require a considerable effort. For the next two sets of this exercise, go for a slightly heavier weight which allows you to repeat the exercise with some extra effort. Use a *spotter* (training partner) to help you with the final reps of each set.

Generally speaking, the weights you start using as a beginner will be governed by your natural build, age, previous athletic experience and genetics. Try a few weights and see how they feel, bearing in mind the principles I have just explained. If the weight is too light or too heavy, try another one. It is not really possible to give the absolute weights you should use since the variation between individuals is so great. While you are learning, use only nominal weights. As you become accustomed to handling them, and familiar with the strength capacity of your body, work heavier. Always push yourself hard, but safely. If you learn a completely new exercise at any level of your training, follow this same guideline because you will be stressing muscles in a new way and they will be weak.

Progression

Progression is not a constant factor. You will notice there are days when you can lift practically anything, and others when for no apparent reason you can't. Daily variations are irrelevant but, once you are past the basic beginner's stage in bodybuilding, you will need to employ a whole variety of techniques to intensify your efforts in order to continue stimulating the muscles sufficiently to make them grow.

Refining your training will help you to overcome sticking points and achieve your long-term objectives. This is why all the more advanced bodybuilding techniques have been developed to push a developed physique to its ultimate potential. In practice, it would be both physically and mentally exhausting to train with maximum intensity for every exercise of every work-out. There are those who advocate that you should – but unless you are a very advanced bodybuilder with years of experience and a highly adapted metabolism, you will not induce growth by training this way all the time but only overtraining, leading to mental and physical breakdown. Most bodybuilders train regularly with sub-maximal weights and reasonable rest intervals. Only occasionally will they push themselves to the limit on one particular exercise or muscle group, in order to find out what their maximum capabilities are.

MUSCLES

Bodybuilders tend to abbreviate the names of the main muscle groups for convenience sake. Here are the most common:

Abs   Abdominal muscles (*rectus abdominis, transversus abdominis, internal and external obliques*).

Delts   Cap of the shoulder where it joins the arms (*deltoids*).

Pecs   Chest muscles supporting the breasts (*pectorals*).

Traps   Large flat triangular muscle of the upper back (*trapezius*).

Lats   Very large muscle of the mid-back section and behind the shoulder, which gives the back its greatest width (*latissimus dorsi*).

Glutes   A group of three muscles which form the buttocks (*gluteals*).

Quads   A group of four muscles in front of the thigh (*quadriceps femoris*) comprising the *sartorius, rectus femoris, vastus lateralis* and *vastus medialis*.

The muscles of the front of the body

The muscles of the back of the body

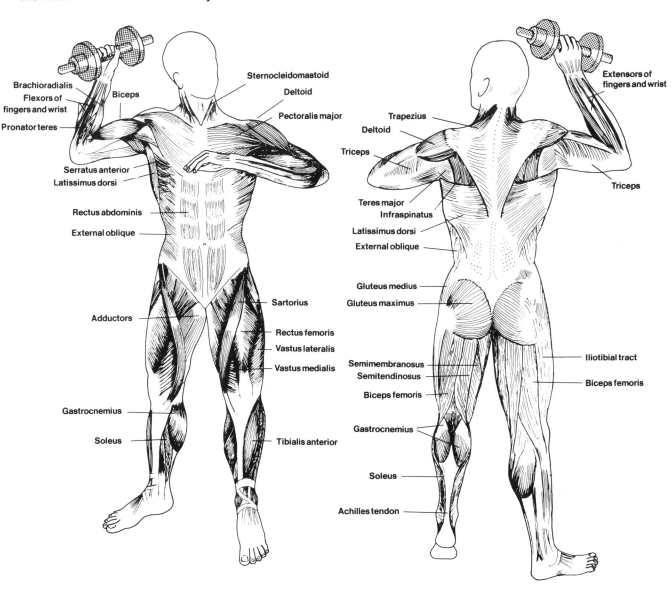

23

Other muscles referred to regularly include the following:

Arms *Biceps*: Large muscle at the front of the upper arm.
Brachialis: Muscle lying beneath the biceps.
Triceps: A muscle group in three sections at the back of the upper arm.
Forearm: The muscle extensors are on the back, and flexors on the front of the forearm.

Chest *Serratus anterior*: Finger-like muscles of the upper chest.

Back *Erector spinae*: The long double line of muscles running the length of the spine.

Legs *Adductors*: Inside thigh muscles.
Biceps femoris (hamstrings): Muscle at the back of the thigh, with two heads, like the arm biceps.
Calf muscles (*gastrocnemius* and *soleus*): The *soleus* is directly underneath the *gastrocnemius*.

Muscles Involved in Movement

1 A muscle primarily involved in a movement is called the '*prime mover*' (e.g. the biceps).

2 A muscle involved in the opposite movement is called the '*antagonist*' or '*opponent*' (e.g. triceps).

3 A muscle which helps a movement indirectly is called a '*synergist*'.

4 Muscles which tense in order to hold joints rigid are called '*stabilizers*'.

5 Muscles are attached to bones by *tendons* and *ligaments*.

THE BASIC PRINCIPLES OF 'STRICT FORM'

1 Exercise the muscle throughout its full range of movement, from full extension to full flexion and back again. Performing an exercise correctly in this way, (in 'strict form'), develops the muscle along its entire length, including the ends where it inserts into the bone, and not just at its midpoint. In competitive bodybuilding, judges look for an even development of this kind, and in terms of everyday life it is important to develop muscle at its limits. It is lifting in the extended position, using muscle at its weakest point, which causes most pulls, tears and sprains. In order to prepare a muscle for weight-training, it is necessary to stretch it first. For bodybuilders to develop their full muscular potential it is essential to incorporate stretching into their work-outs (see pp. 28–30).

2 Eliminate all unnecessary body movement other than those designed to stress the muscle group in action. For instance, if you swing your body backwards as you perform a bicep curl, it becomes an exercise for the back, but ceases to stress the biceps. By taking stress away from the muscles intended, you are *cheating* in bodybuilding terminology and depriving the exercise of much of its benefit.

3 Work slowly and deliberately. Do not swing the weight upwards using impetus to help you as this will take stress away from the muscle. Lower the weight as slowly as you can to its starting point, resisting the pull of gravity all the way. Control the tendency to 'drop' the weight. This negative movement is just as beneficial as the upward lift if performed strictly.

A good way of judging if you are performing an exercise correctly is that the last four reps should be hard to complete. If they are relatively easy, you are either using too little weight, or you are cheating. If you are cheating, you are also probably attempting to lift too much weight too soon. Reduce the weight and repeat the exercise in strict form, and it will be much more beneficial.

CONCENTRATION

Personally, I find it is most important to approach a training session with a positive mental attitude. Make it something that you really look forward to – a period of the day that is yours alone, into which you escape. When you get to the gym don't linger in the changing room chatting to friends, because you can do this later. Get changed quickly and plunge straight into your work-out. Concentrate hard on the job in hand, particularly the muscle you are working. Don't let your mind wander, or be distracted by anyone or anything. When your muscles scream 'Stop, enough!', your mind has to react by saying 'Not a chance'. Psych yourself up with images of your ideal body, of winning the British championship or Miss Olympia, or whatever dream you may have. Some days it will be relatively easy; on others, it will be an out-and-out battle to get to the end of the work-out. Just make sure it is always your mind which wins.

REST INTERVALS

During a heavy work-out, rest for half to one minute between sets to allow your breathing to return to normal. Stay standing up if you can, and keep moving around. Do not rest so long that you become cold and risk injury. On the other hand, allow enough time for the muscles to recover sufficiently to perform the next movement. Some exercises require longer rest intervals than others. If you are performing heavy squats, you will need at least one to one and a half minutes' rest, probably sitting down, whereas exercises for the upper body using dumb-bells will be less taxing, and you could perform a few gentle stretches in between to relax the muscles. If you are training two or three bodyparts during one workout, allow yourself a longer rest when you finish each bodypart – say five minutes. If you are training for a contest or weight-loss, you should rest as little as possible between all reps and sets. This will lead, inevitably, to a reduction in the amount of weight you can handle.

BREATHING

The general rule to follow for all exercises is to breathe in before you start, and out as you make the effort. This is the opposite to the natural instinct and takes a little practice to get used to. If you can get the hang of it while using the beginners' conditioning schedule (pp. 30–41), you will find it much easier when you start to use weights. The reason for special breathing is that the muscles require a good supply of oxygen to produce enough energy and therefore strength to lift a weight. By inhaling, you fill the lungs with oxygen, which is transported by the blood to the muscles, so it is in the right place for you to start. As you exhale, you empty the lungs and can lift the weight more easily as you do so. The forceful expulsion of air gives you extra power for an instant and helps you to lift the weight past the natural sticking point where muscle leverage is weakest.

It is helpful to exaggerate breathing so that you can hear yourself. Always breathe in through the nose, taking in as much air as you can and really expand the lungs. This is particularly important for all chest exercises such as bench press, flyes, incline presses, pull-overs. Exhale through the mouth and blow the air out with force. Do not try to be ladylike. It should sound as if you are blowing up a balloon. In the case of abdominal exercises such as sit-ups and crunches, you will simply not be able to do them with your lungs full of air because you won't be able to bend in the middle. Don't worry if you cannot get the knack of correct breathing straight away. The main thing to remember is to continue breathing, and not to attempt exercises while holding your breath which is quite a common fault with beginners. Two exercises in particular, the squat

and bench press, which eventually involve very heavy weights, must always be done with correct breathing. If you hold your breath for these in certain circumstances you can black out, which could be dangerous.

TRAINING PARTNERS

There are some people who like to work-out with a regular partner, who can act as a spotter; others who prefer to work alone. It depends on you. You will need to find someone who is always available at the same time as you and they will need to work to a similar schedule, at a similar level. Ideally, pick someone who is slightly stronger and more advanced, so they egg you on. One partner is always going to get more out of it than the other for this reason. Sometimes, working-out with a male training partner can be beneficial. He will be working a bit harder to impress you and you will work with heavier weights because you have a strong spotter available. As long as you keep romance out of it, this is a good arrangement. You can't gaze deep into someone's eyes and bench press 120 lbs at the same time with any measure of success in either activity!

SAFETY

Weight-training is a very safe activity if it is carried out correctly and provided that certain basic groundrules are observed.

■ Check all apparatus before you use it. Make sure all bars are evenly loaded and that the collars are in position and firmly secured. Never use a bar for any exercise without retaining collars. The same rule applies to dumb-bells.

■ If you are unloading a series of heavy plates from a bar resting on a squat-rack, make sure someone stands at the opposite end to you and takes the plates off evenly, otherwise the bar might overbalance and the light end could flick up into your face.

■ Check that squat-racks are stable and will not overbalance, and always step backwards from them, not forwards, once you have the bar across your shoulders.

■ Make sure that the distance between the end of bars and the weights is even.

■ Check all bench tops to make sure they are not loose or unattached and watch out for sharp metal edges and loose wires on all equipment.

■ If using multigym or Nautilus machines, keep your fingers away from all moving parts, and watch out for frayed wires and loose retaining pins.

■ Always replace the equipment which is not in use into racks and keep the gym floor uncluttered.

■ Ideally, the gym floor should have a non-slip rubber surface. Carpet, especially frayed, is dangerous.

■ Never train alone. Always have a 'spotter' present.

■ Always warm-up well before you start.

■ Always lift up and put down weights correctly (see p. 43) by bending your knees and keeping your back straight.

■ Always receive a bar or dumb-bells from a spotter with your arms locked-out straight, otherwise they may collapse.

■ Keep your feet flat on the floor for all free weight exercises.

■ Keep to your schedule of exercises and do not try to lift maximum weights without your coach's advice, and a spotter present.

■ Never sacrifice correct form to lift more. Always perform exercises strictly and under control.

■ Do not attempt to compete with others who can lift more. Keep within your own capabilities: you will make progress.

■ Seek expert help if you want to try a new exercise or piece of apparatus. Make sure you know how to use it properly and safely and which muscle or group of muscles it is working.

■ Progress slowly and with enjoyment. If you are bored or miserable, change your exercise schedule or your gym, but do not give up training!

■ *Never* attempt to squat, bench press or lift heavy weights overhead unless you have a spotter.

■ Always receive a bar on the shoulders with a flat back and a slight dip at the knees.

■ Make sure that you never lean backwards. This is the most dangerous move a weight-trainer can make, causing hyper-extension of the back. Be careful of this, too, when doing power-cleans, hyper-extensions, and 'good mornings'.

■ Correct breathing is important. Always breathe *out* as you make the effort. It does not matter if you get it wrong, as long as you don't hold your breath! This causes pressure to build up in the chest and restricts bloodflow to the brain. You could then black-out under a heavy weight.

GENERAL GYM ETIQUETTE

At certain times of the day gyms are often very full of people using heavy equipment and concentrating hard. In order to avoid accidents and maintain a calm atmosphere the instructors usually insist on the following:

■ Never fool around in a gym. Horseplay is dangerous.

■ Don't get in the way of other people or hog the apparatus.

■ Ask to work-out with a group rather than stand around getting cold.

■ Don't drop weights or crash weights around. It is unnecessary and distracting and is a sure sign of an inexperienced trainer. Train quietly with the minimum amount of groans and other sound effects, which are distracting to others.

■ Watch out for other people when moving apparatus, don't collide with them, and keep out of their way.

■ Never interrupt someone halfway through an exercise. If you are performing an exercise, never move for someone else, or reply to a question, until you have finished.

■ If you have no regular training partner, you can always ask politely for someone in the gym to spot for you, if that person is resting between sets. In return, be prepared to spot for others. Be alert to other trainers and volunteer emergency assistance when required.

■ Never show off. Be confident but not reckless.

SPOTTERS

Weight-training in the early stages is a precarious business. You will probably feel uncoordinated and ungainly, your muscles will be unused to it and you will wobble and shake. Your balance will leave much to be desired. Until you learn to handle weights competently, you will need someone standing close by to watch the weights if you fail.

Equally, you may be called upon to be a spotter for someone else, so you will have to learn to lift weights safely. The spotter is in a highly responsible position and when the person training is inexperienced, this is doubly true for their safety depends on the spotter's alertness.

In Chapter 4, I have outlined, alongside the relevant exercise description, exactly what a spotter should be doing to help out. There are certain groundrules which should be applied in all cases:

■ The spotter should be wide awake at all times, watching the action, and not be looking idly around the gym. He should stand close enough to the weight to catch it in an emergency.

- The exerciser is always the one in charge and should issue instructions to the spotter. These should be loud and clear, such as 'Take!' or 'Lift!' or 'Let go now!' or even just 'OK'.
- Spotters should never let go of a bar until instructed to let go by the exerciser.
- Equally, the exerciser should never entirely trust a spotter and should always hang on to the bar or dumb-bell, alongside the spotter, until it is in a safe place (e.g. the rack, or away from your face).
- Beginners performing the squat or bench press should always use two spotters, one on each side.
- Spotters can help the exerciser to push out the final reps which would not be possible working alone. Always use a spotter, at any level of experience, when training to exhaustion, or when using intensifying techniques such as negatives and forced reps.
- As you become more experienced you will be able to dispense with a spotter for some exercises, but remember that a good spotter will develop into a first-class training partner, a very valuable asset for anyone training seriously.

Chapter Four

EXERCISES

WARMING-UP

It is most important to start any exercise programme by warming-up for five to ten minutes. This prepares your body and mind for the work to follow, prevents torn muscles, and helps you get the most out of your work-out. It is especially important to do this in cold weather. Start with a few minutes of aerobics. Jog on the spot, skip, or cycle on a stationary bike for three to five minutes. You can then add any sequence of keep-fit exercises that you choose. For instance, alternate toe touches, push-ups, jumping jacks, body twists or free squats.

A selection of suggested warm-ups

■ **Jog on the spot or skip** for two or three minutes. Start fairly slowly, raising your feet only slightly from the floor. Gradually speed up, and raise your knees higher.

■ **Free squats.** Start with feet apart and hands by your sides. Squat down as low as you can, swinging your arms forward as you do so to balance. Straighten your legs and return to start position. Repeat.

■ **Alternate toe touches.** Stand with feet fairly wide apart. Keeping your legs straight, bend over and twist to the left until you can touch your left foot with your right hand. Stand up, and then repeat to the right side.

■ **Body twists.** Stand with feet apart. Hold out your arms at bust level in front of you. Grasp your hands together so that your elbows are extended. Swing your elbows and upper body to the left as far as possible and then to the right. Repeat. Keep your eyes on the leading elbow as you twist.

■ **Jumping jacks.** From a standing position bend out the knees slightly and spring about six inches from the floor. As you do so, spread your feet to shoulder width, and lift your arms up and over your head till they touch. As you land, spring straight back up again. Repeat.

■ **Push-ups.** Lie on the floor face down, with your legs together. Support your weight on your knees and hands. Bend your arms until your chest touches the floor, then straighten your arms and return to start position. Repeat.

■ **Lunges.** Stand with your hands on your hips and feet slightly apart. Take a wide step forward with your left leg, and bend your knee, 'sitting' into the lunge as you do so with a straight back. Do not let your trailing leg touch the ground at the knee. Straighten the left knee and stand up. Repeat with the right leg.

■ **Sidebends.** Stand with feet apart and hands by the sides. Bend over to the left, and extend your left hand as far down your leg as you can reach. Keep your body facing forward; do not twist. Return to upright position and then repeat on the opposite side.

STRETCHING

The main reasons for including stretching in your training programme are:

1 It improves your capacity for development, by increasing the range of motion through which you can work a muscle.

2 It is an excellent warm-up activity at the beginning and end of a training session. Stretches can be incorporated into the warm-up schedule already described. As a 'cool-down' at the end of a work-out, stretching aids in dispersing exercise waste products and thereby prevents subsequent stiffness, aches and pains caused by their build-up.

3 It prevents injuries due to the overextension of

muscle or connective tissue. This can happen only too easily if a relaxed muscle is stretched too far and too fast.

The ability to stretch well varies widely according to the natural ability of the individual and the type of lifestyle or exercise programme which they follow. On the whole, women are more flexible than men. Many top bodybuilders believe that a very marked improvement in overall physique development can be achieved by including regular stretching in their training programmes.

The Right Way to Stretch

The main thing to remember is to move slowly and carefully into a full stretch, extend the muscles gradually, until you reach the point at which slight pain can be felt in the stretched muscle. Then *stop*. Do not go beyond this point, or you may actually cause tiny muscle tears.

Do not on any account bounce. This movement will cause contraction and therefore shortening of the stretched muscle. The brain, anticipating overextension of the muscle, quickly activates a protective reflex to act as a shock absorber. This is counter-productive to the effect you wish to achieve.

Once you reach the 'pain edge', ease up slightly, wait until the sensation subsides, then gently return to the stretch position. In this position, hold the stretch for between five to thirty seconds. At first, you may find it hard to stretch very far at all in any direction but with regular practice, marked improvement should be rapid. The secret is to be consistent and to stretch daily, trying to push a little further each time. Eventually you should aim to hold each stretch position for one or two minutes, building up the time gradually.

For a good warm-up and flexibility session, one stretch for each body part is ideal, which should take no more than fifteen minutes. Perform each stretch for between five and thirty seconds, working up gradually to one minute. They can be performed in any sequence you prefer.

Stretching Exercises

- **Lunging stretch.** For the hips, buttocks and thighs. Stand upright, with your hands on your hips, then lunge forward on to one knee, as far forward as you can, extending the other leg behind you. Hold the position, then return to start position and repeat with the other leg.

- **Hurdler's stretch.** For the groin and hamstrings. Sit on the floor with one leg extended straight in front of you, and the other behind you, flat on the floor and bent at right angles. Start with your body upright, then lean forward to grasp the ankle in front of you with both hands. Hold. Change over your leg position and repeat.

- **Inner thigh stretch.** For the inner thigh muscles. Sit down on the floor. Bend your legs so that the knees face outwards to the sides, and the soles of the feet are touching. Pull the legs up close to the body and sit upright. Push down your knees outwards, aiming to touch them to the floor on either side.

- **Hamstring stretch.** Stand upright with straight legs. Bend over and touch your toes. Attempt to grasp your ankles from the rear with each hand and, finally, to place both palms flat on the floor. Also, aim to get your upper body tucked closer in to your knees, so that eventually your chest actually touches your knees when you clasp your legs.

- **Shoulder stretch.** Stand upright with straight legs, holding a broomstick behind you with both hands, across the back of your thighs. Bend over forward and, with straight arms, lift the broomstick up and over your head, and as far in front of you as you can reach. Hold. Return to start position. Repeat.

- **Cat stretch.** For the back and abdominal muscles. Start on all fours on the floor. Rise up on to your toes and hands, and arch your back. Pull in your stomach muscles. Now, keeping your arms and legs straight, lower your hips to the floor, and lean forward, so your back is concave. Keep your head up and back. Hold.

- **Sidebend stretch.** For oblique muscles at the side of the waist. Stand upright with feet apart. Hold your arms upright over your head, with clasped hands. Keeping your pelvis facing forward throughout, bend over as far as you can manage, first to one side, then to the other.

- **Spinal stretch.** For the back and general stretch of the whole body. Jump up to grasp a chinning bar (or tree branch, etc.) and simply hang from it, until your arms fail. Very relaxing at any time!

- **Calf stretch.** Stand upright, with hands on hips. Extend one leg out behind you, as far as possible, in a reverse lunge position. Press the heel down gently into the ground. Keep extending your leg further back as it becomes easier to get your foot flat.

- **Neck stretch.** Tilt your head forward until your chin touches your chest, then roll it to the right side to rest on your shoulder, then to the rear, and finally to the left shoulder. Carry on going round in a circular motion. Repeat, going in the opposite direction.

This short selection of stretches is only a limited sample from the hundreds available. You should experiment to find ones which you enjoy doing or which your body requires more than others, depending on your personal area of inflexibility.

BEGINNERS' PRE-WEIGHT-TRAINING SCHEDULE FOR CONDITIONING

This introductory section is devoted to descriptions of thirteen exercises for use in a pre-weight-training conditioning schedule. (The work-out programme which goes with them, is described in Chapter 5, p. 89–90.)

Sit-Ups (a)

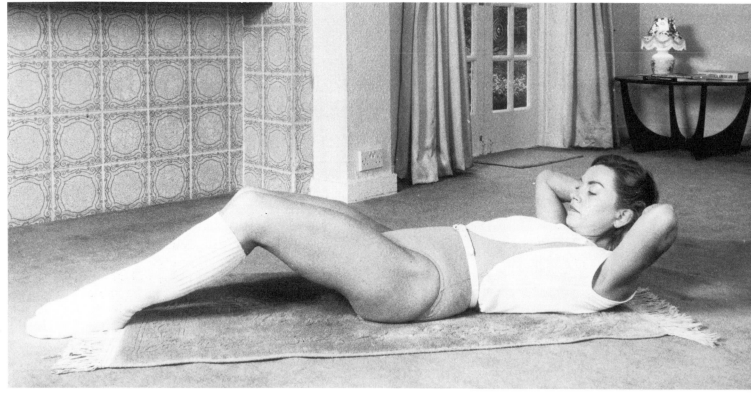

(b)

1. *Sit-Ups*

EXERCISE STRESS: The upper stomach muscles (abdominals).

What To Do
Lie on the floor, with your feet hooked under some furniture or held down by a training partner. Place your hands behind your head and keep your elbows out to the sides. Your head and shoulders should be off the floor throughout. Bend your knees slightly and keep them in this position, to take strain off your lower back. Sit up slowly and bend over as far as you can reach. Try to touch your knees with your nose. Have a good stretch, hold it for a moment, then slowly lie down again, replacing one vertebra at a time on the floor. Do not collapse, keep the tension on your mid-section throughout. Repeat as ability permits. Don't overdo it.

Tips
If you cannot perform this exercise with your hands behind your head, rest them on the front of your thighs as you sit up.

Perform the whole movement slowly. Do not flap up and down using momentum.

If you have any kind of back pain, this is an inadvisable exercise to perform. If it hurts, don't do it. This is a good general rule to follow for any exercise. There are lots of other alternatives. Here is one:

Half Jack-Knives

What To Do
Sit on the floor with your hands lightly supporting you on either side, just behind your bottom. Lean back slightly. With your feet together, bring your knees up to your chest and, at the same time, sit up straight to meet them. Extend your legs straight out in front of you, keeping feet and knees together and lean backwards for about 45° as you do so. Keep your feet close to the ground throughout, and do not touch down at full extension.

Tip
To make it harder, take your hands off the floor.

2. *Leg-Raises*

EXERCISE STRESS: The lower abdominal muscles of the stomach. This is the weakest area of the body for most women, so you will probably find this exercise difficult. At first, you may only be able to do about 5 reps. Don't worry, this is quite usual, and luckily the stomach muscles are the fastest to recover from exercise and gain strength.

What To Do
Lie down on the floor and place your hands behind your head. Raise your head and shoulders off the floor and maintain this position throughout. With your feet together, slowly raise your legs off the ground to the vertical position. Keeping your knees very slightly bent to take strain off the lower back, slowly lower them back down to the floor. Stop about

Half Jack-Knives (a)

(b)

two inches from ground-level and raise the legs again. Continue until you cannot repeat the movement. If you can only do a few reps, have a rest, then do a few more until you really cannot do another. Each time you exercise, aim to increase the number of reps you can do without a break. When you can do fifteen easily, increase to sets of twenty-five to thirty. Really push yourself with this exercise. It is horrible, but it pays off. Lots of sit-ups and leg raises mean a flat stomach. In a few months, in combination with a sensible diet, you should lose

inches in this area. Unfortunately, there is no short-cut. You will only get out of it what you put in, so work hard for results.

3. *Twists*

EXERCISE STRESS: This exercise will work the muscles which pull in the sides of the waist, thereby making it smaller, increasing mobility in the hips and also loosening up the lower back.

Leg-Raises (a)

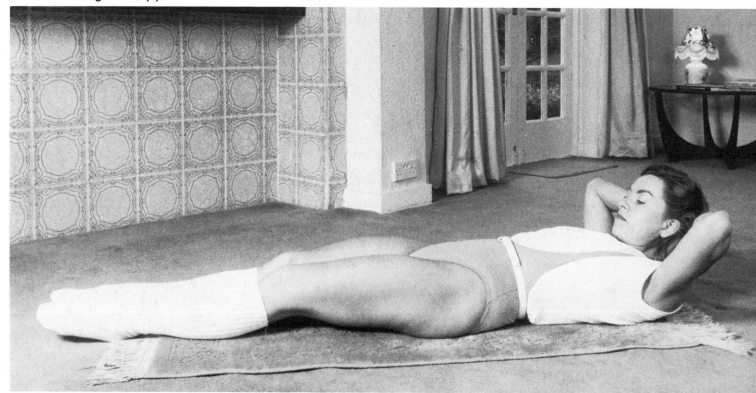

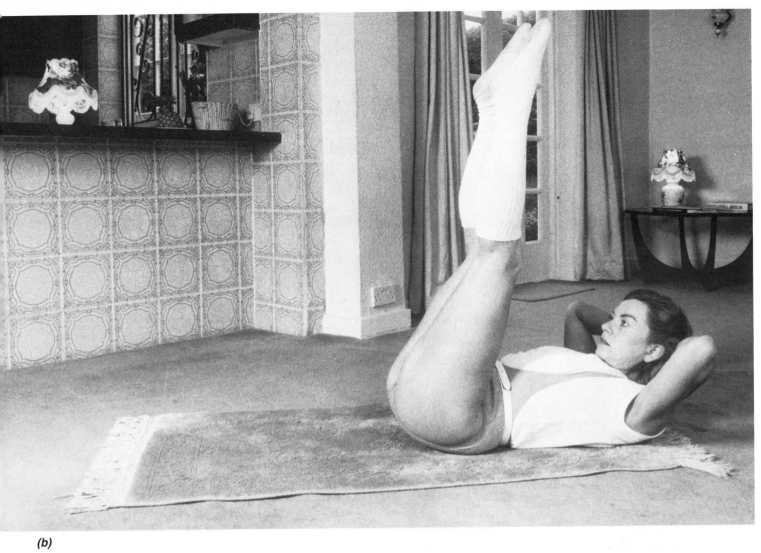

(b)

Seated Twists (a)

(b)

Twists

What To Do

Take an old broom handle and hold it across your shoulders with your hands hanging over the ends, rather than gripping the bar. Stand with your feet about 12 inches apart, face forward, and bend your knees slightly. Keep your hips facing forward. Twist quickly from left to right and back again. Look straight ahead throughout the exercise and keep your back absolutely straight. Now repeat the movement as fast as you can. I usually carry on for about five to ten minutes.

Tips

If you find it hard to keep your hips still, sit astride a bench and lock your feet together (the illustration shows this variation). As this exercise is intended to increase mobility between the upper and lower body, it will not work if you move your hips as well as your torso.

Most women find they are very inflexible at first and cannot twist very far. Persevere. Eventually you should be able to twist around far enough to see the middle of your back reflected in a mirror.

4. *Free Squats*

EXERCISE STRESS: Primarily the legs, but it also involves major muscle groups in the back, stomach and arms, and is a good general conditioning exercise. It specifically stresses the front of the thighs and the muscles of the buttocks (*gluteus maximus*). When you start to squat with weights, this will be an ideal warm-up exercise.

What To Do

Start with your legs 12 inches apart, and feet facing forward. Keep your back flat and chin up. Squat down as low as possible. At the same time, swing your arms forward to waist level, to balance you. Keep your heels flat on the floor. Stand up again and let your arms drop down by your sides. Repeat.

Tip

You may find it difficult to keep your heels down, which can cause you to overbalance. This is because women who habitually wear high heels have shortened Achilles tendons. In time, you will gain flexibility but in the beginning it will help if you raise your heels on a block of wood.

Free Squats (a)

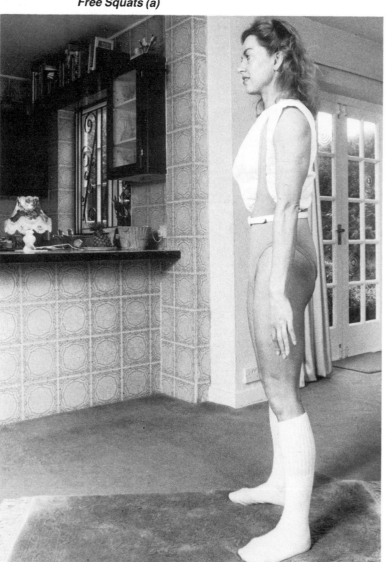

(b)

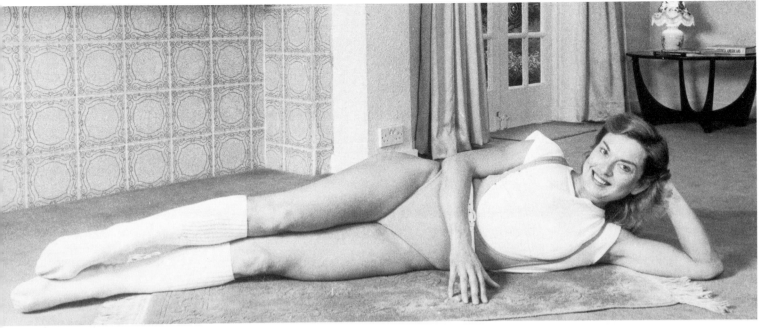

Side Leg-Raises (a)

(b)

5. *Side Leg-Raises*

EXERCISE STRESS: The outside of the thighs, and the
buttock muscles (*gluteus maximus*).

What To Do
Lie on your side, supporting your weight on one arm
in front of you. Straighten out your body. Raise your
upper leg as high as you can with the foot flexed,
then lower it. Repeat. Change over to the other side
and repeat with the other leg. To increase
resistance, you can wear ankle-weights.

6. *Back Leg-Raises*

EXERCISE STRESS: The hamstrings and buttocks (leg biceps and *gluteus maximus*).

What To Do
Kneel on all fours and lower your head until it touches the floor, holding it in your clasped hands.

Raise your right leg straight up from the floor, as high as you can, keeping the foot flexed throughout, then lower it back down to the start position. Do not bend your leg at any point. Repeat with each leg in turn.

Tip
To increase resistance, wear ankle-weights.

Back Leg-Raises (a)

(b)

7. *Inner Thigh-Raises*

EXERCISE STRESS: The inner thigh muscles (adductors).

What To Do

Select a bench or chair with no obstructions underneath it. Lie on your side, making sure your body is in a straight line. Support your weight with one hand in front of you. Put your uppermost foot on the bench top or chair seat, then raise the other leg, underneath the bench or chair, to meet it. Repeat quickly with each leg in turn.

Tip

To increase resistance, wear ankle-weights.

Inner Thigh-Raises (a)

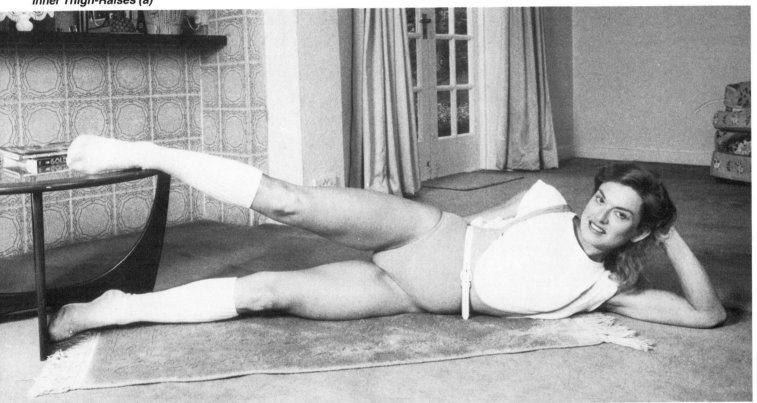

(b)

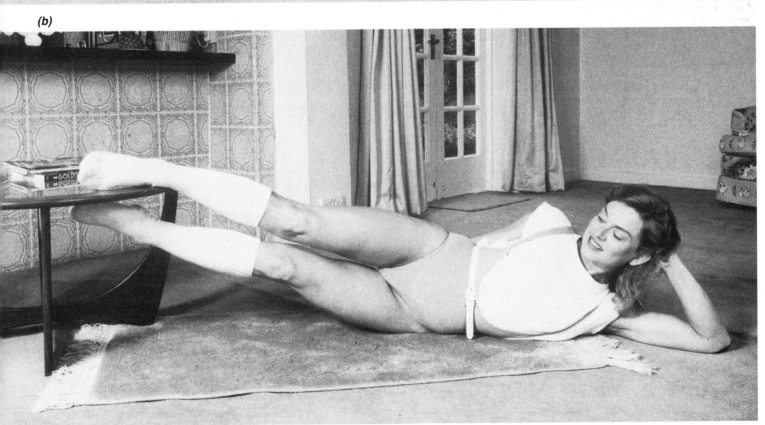

8. *Flyes*

EXERCISE STRESS: The chest muscles which support the breasts (pectorals). This is a good exercise for women, since it helps to firm and tone the bust, and can correct sagging.

What To Do
Hold a large tin, or washing-up liquid container filled with water, or sand, in each hand. Stand with your legs about 12 inches apart. Hold the weights at chest level in front of you, touching each other and, with your elbows slightly bent, extend your elbows out to the sides as far as you can. Return to the start position, crossing the arms over if possible. Repeat.

Variation
If you are not strong enough to move the weights in this position the exercise can be done lying down.

9. *Shrugs*

EXERCISE STRESS: The shoulders (deltoids and trapezius). This exercise is especially beneficial for improving your posture and is a good loosening-up exercise if you are very stiff and tense in the shoulders.

What To Do
Hold a light weight in each hand, then stand upright with your feet slightly apart. Raise your shoulders up as high as you can as if trying to touch your ears. Hold this position for a count of one, then push your shoulders as far back as you can, and then downwards in a rolling movement. Repeat.

Flyes (a)

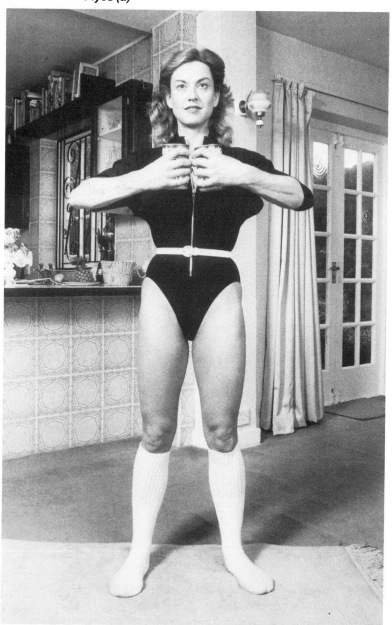

(b)

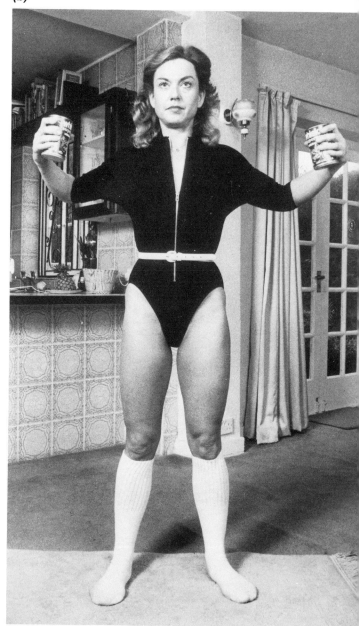

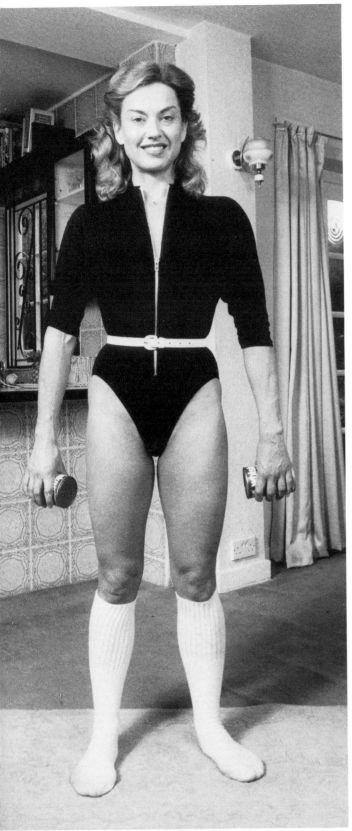

Shrugs (a)

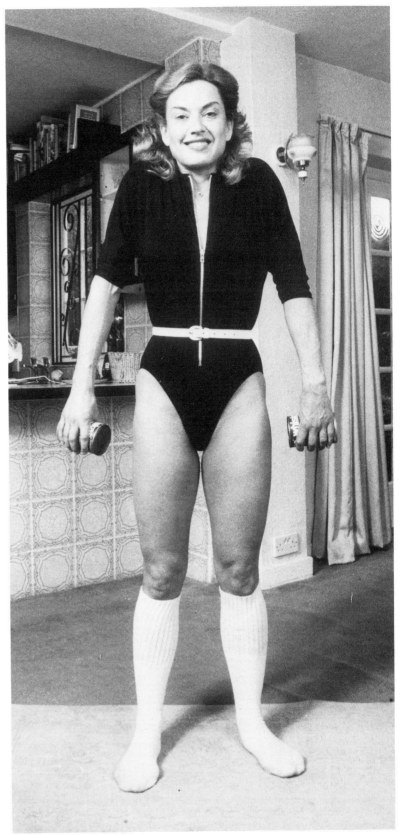

(b)

10. *Side Lateral Raises*

EXERCISE STRESS: The muscles at the junction of the upper arms and shoulders (deltoids).

What To Do
Hold a light weight in each hand, by your sides.

Stand with your feet apart, then raise your arms to the sides until they reach shoulder level. Hold for a count of one and return slowly to start position. Repeat.

Side Lateral Raises (a)

(b)

11. *Good Mornings*

EXERCISE STRESS: The lower back and hamstrings (erector spinae and leg biceps).

What To Do
Hold a broom handle across your shoulders. Start

with your feet apart and straight legs. Bend over slowly until you are at right angles to your legs with your back flat and chin up. Then slowly return to the upright position. Perform this exercise slowly. Repeat.

Biceps Curls (a)

(b)

12. *Biceps Curls*

EXERCISE STRESS: The muscles on the front of the upper arm (biceps).

What To Do
Hold a light weight in each hand, so that they touch the outside of your thighs. Stand with your feet apart and keep your back straight and stable. Tuck your elbows tightly into the sides of your waist and keep them there throughout the exercise. Slowly raise your forearms in a curling movement until you can touch your shoulders with the weights. Hold for a count of one at the top, then slowly lower back to start position. Repeat.

13. *Reverse Arm Push-Ups*

EXERCISE STRESS: The muscles on the back of the upper arm (triceps).

What To Do
Select a low step or bench. Sit on the floor with your back to the bench. With hands reversed, grip the bench behind you. Keep your legs straight out in front of you, then lower your bottom slowly to the ground by bending your arms. Push back up again to the start position, by straightening your arms. Repeat.

Tip
The triceps muscles are usually very weak in most women, so you will probably find this difficult at first. Start with a very low step and work up to higher positions.

Reverse Arm Push-Ups (a)

(b)

BODYBUILDING EXERCISES

The weight-training exercises described in this chapter are a tiny fraction of the hundreds of variations which exist. However, they represent the minimum basic repertoire for any regular weight-trainer or bodybuilder. You do not need to know or to perform endless variants. If you stick to the basics, in time you will make good progress but you can add extra exercises as you learn them, to add variety and interest.

The exercises are grouped together according to bodyparts, and arranged in the sequence in which they would normally appear in a schedule (see Chapter 5), starting with major muscle groups, graduating down to the smaller ones. I have described the heavy basic exercises first, and then the isolation exercises which follow.

There is no need to perform all these exercises all the time. You will need to select and arrange them into a work-out programme to suit your own requirements, perhaps with the advice of your gym instructor. Read Chapter 5 to see how this is done, and refer also to the section on basic and isolation exercises below.

BASIC AND ISOLATION EXERCISES

All bodybuilding exercises can be divided into two major groups, **basic** and **isolation**.

The basic exercises involve the largest muscles of the body in groups. These are used primarily for building muscular depth and bulk, strength and power. **The isolation exercises** work on individual muscles, or even parts of a muscle, and are used primarily for shaping. Because they are used for detail work, much less weight can be used when performing them. Prior to a contest, this type of exercise is increasingly incorporated into a programme, using lower weights and higher reps for definition and fat-burning.

Most training programmes benefit from a combination of the two forms of exercise. A basic exercise should always be performed first for each bodypart, followed by isolation exercises.

A competitive bodybuilder concentrates on using basic exercises for off-season work-outs and adds an increasing number of isolation exercises as a contest approaches. However, a well-designed pre-contest period should still include some basic exercises to maintain muscular bulk.

Here is a list of the more common exercises:

Basic Exercises

1 **Legs:** Front and back squats, leg presses.
2 **Lats.:** Barbell bentover rowing, seated rowing, T-bar rowing, chins, lat. pulldowns.
3 **Shoulders (Traps):** Upright rowing, military press, dumb-bell shoulder press.
4 **Chest:** (Flat/incline/decline) bench press, presses of all types (incline or decline).
5 **Deltoids:** Press behind neck, dumb-bell presses.
6 **Lower Back:** Deadlifts.
7 **Biceps:** Barbell curls, barbell preacher curls.
8 **Triceps:** Lying triceps extensions, close grip bench press, French press.
9 **Calves:** Standing or seated calf-raises.
10 **Abs.:** Leg-raises and sit-ups.

Isolation Exercises

Here is a selection of some of the most familiar and commonly used isolation exercises:

1 **Legs:** Leg extension, leg curls.
2 **Lats.:** One arm rowing, pull-over, close grip pulldowns.
3 **Shoulders (Traps):** Shrugs.
4 **Chest:** Dumb-bell flyes (flat/incline/decline), pec. dec. flyes.
5 **Deltoids:** Front laterals, side laterals, bentover laterals, front-raises.
6 **Lower Back:** Hyperextensions, good mornings.
7 **Biceps:** Concentration curls, cable or dumb-bell curls. Incline dumb-bell curls.
8 **Triceps:** One arm triceps extension, pulley pushdown.
9 **Calves:** Single leg-raises.
10 **Abs.:** Crunches, twists.

CORRECT LIFTING TECHNIQUE

One of the most important safety rules is to know how to lift a weight from the floor and put it down safely. It is amazing how few people know how to lift correctly in everyday life, with the inevitable consequences in terms of back pain, injury and sick leave. The basic lifting principles apply just as much to boxes of groceries, children, furniture and gardening work, as to barbells in the gym.

The Basic Lift

What To Do

Position yourself in front of the barbell with your feet underneath it 12–18 inches apart. Squat down and take hold of the bar with an overhand grip, hands approximately shoulder-width apart. Keep your back flat and taut and your chin up. Stand up, using your powerful thigh muscles. Do not raise your bottom in the air first. Keep your arms relaxed, using them only as hooks for the weight and not for strength assistance. In no circumstances *ever* bend your back when lifting anything. This will put all the stress on the vertebral discs of the lower back, causing almost inevitable injury.

When you put the weight down, repeat the procedure in reverse. Bend your legs and squat down, with knees apart, keeping your head up and back flat. It may not look very elegant, but it is a safe, strong position.

Once you start weight-training, you *must* lift correctly on each and every occasion, without fail, however light the weight, until it becomes automatic. Every bad habit you pick up as a beginner will be a potential cause of injury and danger once you begin to handle a heavier workload later on. It is essential to be constantly aware of correct exercise form right from the start.

Before you start any heavy exercise for a bodypart, always perform one warm-up set using a light weight, for 15 to 20 reps, to get the blood flowing into the area, and everything into working order. Also, read all the exercise descriptions carefully, and look at the illustrations. Bear in mind all the safety principles described in Chapter 3, pp. 25–26. Then plunge in – and happy lifting!

Power-Cleans

The power-clean is an excellent warm-up exercise. It is listed here first because it is the correct way to lift a barbell from the floor to your chest, in preparation for many other exercises (e.g. military presses).

Power-Cleans (a)

(b)

EXERCISE STRESS: This exercise is for all-round body conditioning since it affects the major muscle groups. It particularly stresses the trapezius and lower back muscles and is an excellent mass builder for these areas.

What To Do

Place a barbell in front of you and tuck your feet well underneath it, shoulder-width apart. Squat down with a flat back and take an overhand shoulder-width grip on the barbell. In the starting position, your shoulders should be higher than your hips and your hips higher than your knees. Keep your arms quite straight and your chin up. Pull hard on the bar and, with arms still straight, lift the bar, keeping it as close as possible to the bodyline.

Begin to stand up, by first straightening your legs, then your back. Pull up the bar as you rise, still with straight arms, keeping it close to your body. The whole movement of standing and lifting should be

dynamic, so that the bar is partially lifted by momentum. At the top of the lift, rise up on your toes, then whip your elbows under the bar and catch it at your shoulders. Dip to absorb the shock. To lower the barbell to the floor, take it from the shoulders to the thighs while standing, then bend the knees to replace it on the floor.

To perform a set of power-cleans, repeat without a break between reps. You should be able to lift a relatively heavy weight with this exercise.

LEG EXERCISES

1. *Squats*

Squats are one of the most important basic exercises in the weight-training repertoire and are an integral part of any serious training programme for bodybuilders and athletes alike.

Squats (a)

(b)

EXERCISE STRESS: Primarily these exercises stress the major muscle group in the thighs (the quadriceps) but they also involve the hips and the buttocks. You should remember that heavy exercises such as squats burn up the calories. As you work your thighs heavily, you may at first experience an increase in size as the muscles grow and push out the fat. This alarms many women, but continued heavy training will burn this fat off after a while and replace it with shapely muscle.

Squats are an extremely good general conditioning exercise, since they also involve, in a secondary capacity, the major muscle groups of the abdomen and lower back. The exercise is very strenuous and makes considerable demands on the cardio-vascular system, thereby adding a heart–lung conditioning element as well. Although squats are never popular, probably qualifying as one of the least favourite exercises, they are indispensable and should never be avoided.

Safety Points

Never perform this exercise alone. Always make sure that there are one or more spotters available who are sufficiently strong to assist you if you get into difficulty. The spotter(s) can help you perform extra repetitions by holding the bar from the rear and giving a slight push upwards at the bottom of the lift if you begin to fail.

Wear a wide leather lifting belt for this exercise. It will give you extra abdominal and lower back support, help you maintain an upright position and increase your confidence.

What To Do

Place a long barbell on a squat rack or stand, at a level slightly below your shoulder-height. Load the bar with plates according to your requirements and firmly attach the retaining collars. Check that the plates are evenly loaded. Position yourself under the barbell with your spotter standing behind you (or, in the case of a beginner, one spotter each end of the bar). Place the bar across your shoulders at the base of your neck in a comfortable position. (You can pad the bar with a small towel if you wish.) Grasp the bar each side of your head firmly, with your hands equidistant between the plates and your shoulders. Your feet should be approximately shoulder-width apart with your toes facing slightly outwards. Keep them flat on the floor all the time. Lift the bar from the rack, and step carefully back, about one pace. Keep your back flat and tense the muscles, keep your chin up and fix your eyes on a point high up on the wall throughout the entire movement, take a deep breath, and slowly bend your legs, going down to a thighs-parallel position. Your knees should spread out slightly in line with your toes. Don't try to do this exercise with your legs together! At the

lowest point, do not bounce or linger, but come straight back up again with dynamic force, exhaling as you do so, which will give you extra power. Concentrate on your thigh muscles all the time, and nothing else. Take another deep breath and repeat the movement for the required number of repetitions.

Tips

Whatever you do, **never** bend your back. Keep tight and upright all the time. If you lose your nerve or strength, in an emergency throw the bar off backwards and don't collapse forwards with it on top of you, bearing in mind, of course, the location of your spotter.

If you have tight tendons, you may find it hard to keep your heels flat. If so, prop them up on a block until you develop your flexibility. Do not continue to use this aid once you progress to heavier weights as it would be hazardous.

Exercise Variations

There is a great deal of controversy regarding the most effective way of performing squats. Some people maintain that a full squat, performed as low as possible, will injure your knee joints. This may be true if you are a weightlifter or powerlifter constantly using maximum weights, but with bodybuilding weights, you will merely aid your flexibility. It is worth remembering that the lower you go, the more you will involve your gluteal muscles (your backside), and if you want what an American I know calls a 'pedigree ass', this is the way to get it.

If you squat halfway down, or quarter squat, you will stress the quadriceps more directly. This type of partial squat can be very beneficial. You will be able to use much more weight since you are not so reliant on the strength of your joints and tendons. Always make sure you have strong spotters nearby. You can also place a bench underneath you and go down only as far as the bench each rep. This adds a certain feeling of security, but it can become a crutch.

Varying the position of your feet also stresses different areas of the thighs. A wider stance will build the inner thigh but be careful of this because too much muscular development in this area will make your legs press together in the middle, giving a fatter impression. The most flattering thigh area for a woman to develop is the outer sweep from the knee to the hip. This can be best achieved by squatting with a narrow stance, with toes facing more forwards.

For overall development, vary your depth of squat, and your stance regularly.

Front Squats are a variation much favoured by some bodybuilders. In this exercise the bar is held across the chest, with crossed arms. It can be very awkward if you have a large bustline but it does stress the outer quads very effectively.

2. *Leg Extensions*

To perform this exercise you will need to use a leg extension machine in the gym. This is one of the most basic pieces of exercise equipment available and should be readily accessible.

EXERCISE STRESS: This is an isolation exercise which concentrates stress on the quadriceps muscles of the thigh.

What To Do
Before you start, select your weight and adjust the pin in the weight stack according to your requirements. Sit on the edge of the machine with your feet hooked under the padded rollers and the back of your knees pressed against the end of the bench. Grip the padded top of the bench firmly with your hands on each side of your seat. Keep your back very straight. Raise your weighted legs slowly until they are locked out straight. At the top of the lift, hold briefly, then slowly lower your legs back down to the starting position, resisting gravity all the way. Repeat for the required number of reps.

Tip
Make certain you exercise through the full range of movement, allowing the legs to return right down to

Leg Extensions

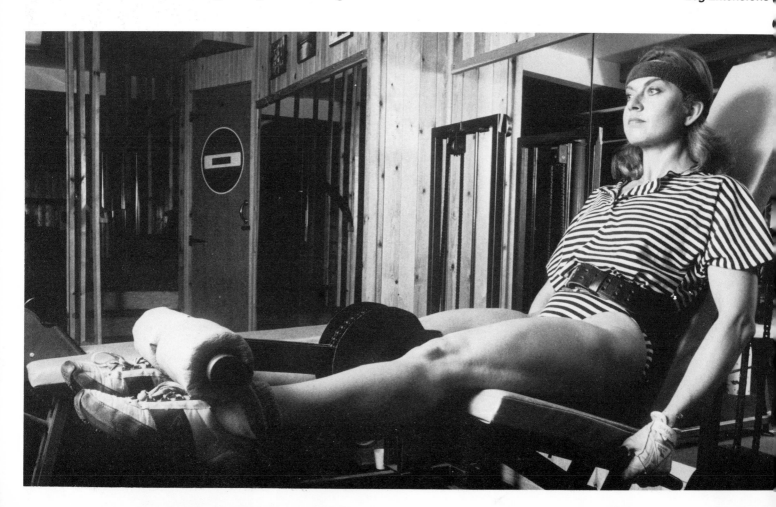

the starting point, and lock out straight at the top. There is always a temptation to stop and start short or bounce to make it easier. This will reduce stress on the areas you wish to reach, and cheat you of maximum benefit. Always make each exercise as difficult as possible for yourself, then you can be certain you are doing it in strict form.

Variations
This exercise can be performed with only one leg at a time, which makes it harder but easier to coordinate. This principle applies to any other exercise, whether of the arms or legs.

You can use iron boots or ankle-weights instead of a machine.

There is an excellent Nautilus leg extension machine which can be used if you have access to the facility. It is very similar to the free weight leg extension machine but has the advantage of providing even stress throughout the range of movement.

3. *Leg Curls*

EXERCISE STRESS: This is the primary isolation exercise for the hamstrings (*biceps femoris*) at the back of the thigh. This muscle is usually quite weak and you will not be able to use very much weight for this exercise. In many gyms, the leg extension and leg curl machines are combined in one piece of apparatus.

Leg Curls (a)

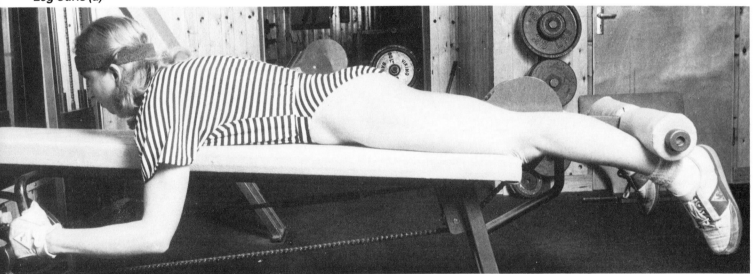

(b)

Leg Curls

What To Do
Select the weight you require on the leg curl machine and adjust the pin accordingly. Lie face down on the padded bench of the machine. Position your heels under the padded rollers, grasp the sides of the bench each side of your head firmly and keep your head down. Raise your feet slowly, until they are at 90° to your body. Slowly lower them back to the starting position. Be sure to use the full range of movement available to you on this machine and do not stop short of full extension or full flexion. If you are using a Nautilus leg curl machine, it will compensate for you.

Tip
Concentrate on keeping your hips pressed firmly down into the bench throughout. Do not cheat by letting your bottom rise. By doing so, you cease to stress the leg biceps, and involve the glutes. This might indirectly help develop them, but that is not what this exercise is intended to achieve.

Variations
As with leg extensions, you can perform this exercise one leg at a time which markedly increases the intensity of the movement and makes it easier to concentrate on correct form.

Leg Presses (a)

4. Leg Presses

EXERCISE STRESS: This is a basic heavy mass-building exercise, stressing the quadriceps, glutes and hips. Because it is a machine not a free weight exercise, no element of balance or skill is required. It does not involve all the synchronistic and stabilizer muscles which squatting does. For this reason it is somewhat safer to perform and does not stress the lower back. Anyone with a back problem would be better advised to stick to leg presses.

What To Do
Adjust the weights on the machine to your personal requirements. Remember that the muscles you will be working are some of the most powerful in the body and are used to carrying about your bodyweight. Therefore do not be timid about piling on the weight. Most women can handle 100 kilos upwards without difficulty.

Method 1: Lie on your back underneath the machine with your hips pulled right up to the padded base. Grasp the handles on each side of you. Place your feet on the bar above you, shoulder-width apart. Your knees should be resting against your chest in the start position. Slowly straighten your legs, then lower them slowly back to the starting position, on your chest, resisting gravity throughout. Repeat for the required number of reps.

(b)

Method 2: Some multigym machines do not have a vertical leg press but instead have a machine with a horizontal action. In this variation you sit in an adjustable seat with your feet resting on pedals.

First of all, select the weight you require and adjust the pin. Adjust the seat position so your knees touch your chest, grasp the handles each side of you, place your feet on the pedals and push hard, until your legs are almost straight. Sit upright throughout. Don't lock out your knees completely, as this will reduce the intensity of the movement. Bend your knees and slowly return to start position. Repeat.

Variation

This exercise can be done one leg at a time and the position of the feet can be varied to stress different areas of the thighs.

5. Hack Squats

EXERCISE STRESS: This is an isolation exercise for the front of the thigh and is particularly important for developing an attractive sweep to the outer quads just above the knee.

What To Do

There are several variations on the design of the hack-squat machine, but the usual type has a sloping padded surface against which you lean.

Before you start, adjust the pin in the weight stack to your desired level. Position yourself with your feet on the sloping board at the base of the machine, shoulder-width apart. Firmly grasp the handles on each side and squat down low. Slowly straighten your legs under resistance, leaning well back against the machine as you do so, then bend your legs and return slowly back down to the start position.

Variations

You can vary the position of your feet, as you might with a normal squat or leg-press exercise, to stress different areas of the thigh.

6. Lunges

EXERCISE STRESS: This exercise is a really good one for a variety of reasons. It is used by bodybuilders primarily before competitions in order to shape the thighs and buttocks. It is not a mass-building exercise like squats. It is hard work but in a totally different way. The exercise provides an excellent stretch for the hamstrings and inner thigh and gets right into the quads, emphasizing definition.

Lunges will give a nicely rounded contour to the backside, lifting and firming the area which overhangs. If your legs and backside leave a lot to be desired, this is a good exercise to include in your programme all the time.

What To Do

Lunges are not easy to perform at first. Most women find that the muscles stressed are relatively weak so it may be necessary to begin without any weight at all, except your own bodyweight. You will not be

Lunges (a)

(b)

able to use anything like as much weight as you would for squats.

An extra hazard is the need to balance – I find this really hard due to an ancient ankle injury. If a balance problem persists, perform the exercise with a dumb-bell in each hand, instead of using a barbell. You can adjust the weight more easily if you begin to wobble. Watching yourself in the mirror will also help you to balance upright.

Select a suitably light barbell, and place it across your shoulders in a comfortable position low down at the back of your neck, grip the bar equidistant between your shoulders and the plates. Your feet should be about 12 inches apart, with toes facing forwards.

Starting with your left foot, lunge forward about three feet until your leading knee is a few inches ahead of the foot on the same side. Your trailing leg should be extended as straight as possible behind you. Don't let the knee touch the floor. In this position you should feel a really good stretch in the legs. Push back to the start position until you are standing upright again.

Now repeat the movement with the other leg, and continue alternately until you complete the set.

7. *Inner and Outer Thighs*

EXERCISE STRESS: The adductor muscles of the inner thighs, and the abductor muscles of the outer thighs and hips.

These are difficult muscle groups to exercise and require the use of either a cable machine or the extremely effective Nautilus machines especially designed for these areas.

What To Do
Method 1: The Adductor Muscles
Fix the cable to the ankle next to the machine by means of the attachment cuff. Hang on to a piece of equipment and stand upright balancing on your other leg, well away from the pulley machine. Now let the weighted cable raise your ankle up into the start position. Move it slowly down, using the inner thigh muscles, until it rests in front of your supporting leg. Allow it to be pulled slowly back to the start position to the side. Repeat with the other leg.

Method 1: The Abductor Muscles
Fix the cable to the ankle furthest from the machine this time, so that the wire crosses over in front of your body. Raise the leg as high as possible, using the outer thigh muscles. Let the machine pull the leg back down slowly, and well across the leg on which you are supported. Repeat with each leg for the required number of times.

Method 2
This exercise is most efficiently performed on the specialized Nautilus machines for the purpose.

The Nautilus Adductor Machine is designed so you can force your thighs together under weighted resistance. Having pre-set the required weight, sit in the machine and fasten the seatbelt. Position your legs in the retaining rests, as wide apart as you can stretch. Now push them together until they touch in the middle. Hold, then slowly let them return to maximum stretch. Repeat.

The Nautilus Abductor Machine works in the reverse manner. It enables you to force your thighs apart under weighted resistance. Pre-set the required weight. Sit in the machine and fasten the lapstrap. This time, your legs will be together at the start of the exercise. Push them slowly apart, as wide as you can manage, hold, then slowly return to the start position. Each time you repeat the exercise, try to push your legs apart to the same point. You can keep your eye on a floor crack, or carpet pattern to guide you.

CHEST EXERCISES

8. *Bench Presses*

Together with the squat, this is one of the most fundamental weight-training exercises of all. It is a basic heavy movement for building mass and strength and involves the pectoral muscles of the chest, the triceps and the deltoids, and to a secondary extent the *latissimus dorsi*. Because this exercise is responsible for firming up the muscles which support the chest, it is very important for women.

Safety Tip
This exercise should *never* be attempted when you are alone. The bar could crash down across your throat and fatal accidents have occurred, so always make sure you have a spotter available.

What To Do
a. Free Weight Bench Press
The equipment for performing a bench press consists of a flat bench with an adjustable rack at one end on which the barbell rests. Start by placing the bar on the rack, and then load it with the plates you require. Add the retaining collars and check them for safety.

Lie on the bench with your back flat and your feet flat on the floor each side of the bench. Your eyes should be directly underneath the bar. Grasp the barbell with a shoulder-width grip. Check that the bar is evenly spaced between the supports. (The shiny section between the knurlings will guide you.)

Bench Presses (a)

(b)

With your spotter positioned close behind you, take the bar off the rack with his/her assistance. Lock out your arms and, when you are ready, instruct her to let go. Now you are on your own. Lower the bar slowly down to your chest. Let it touch lightly, then push it back up again powerfully. Keep your back flat on the bench throughout. Never arch it to help you lift as this will take all the stress away from the areas you want to work. Lock out your arms. Repeat.

Safety Tips
If you find you are struggling at the bottom of the lift, get your spotter to give a little assistance at this point. As you get tired, your spotter should keep her hands supportively under the bar at all times, ready to catch if you suddenly fail. Hang on to the bar with the spotter until it is back in the rack. Never, ever, rely on anyone until you are entirely safe.

b. *Machine Bench Presses*
Multigym machines invariably have a bench press station in the form of rigid metal handles, under which you lie on the bench. Pre-set the machine weight, then take up the same position as you would for the free weight exercise. Exhale as you push upwards with the weight, inhale as you lower.

Obviously, the advantage of using a machine for the bench press is that it is safer. You do not need a spotter and you eliminate the elements of skill, balance and coordination. It always seems harder to lift as much weight on a machine. This is because it isolates the relevant muscles more effectively and cuts out assistive muscle action.

Exercise Variation
The principal variation is to change the width of your grip on the bar. A wide grip places most stress on the front deltoids and the outer pectorals. A *narrow grip bench press* is used for working the triceps and inner pectorals.

9. *Incline and Decline Bench Presses*
The bench press is such a fundamental exercise that it is not surprising that it should provide the basis for a whole range of other related movements.

The principal variation is to perform the pressing movement at an angle rather than while lying on a flat bench. This can be done either in an inclined, or upright position, or in a declined, or upside-down position. Most good gyms have the necessary equipment for these two variations, often combined in one sloping bench with a rack at each end.

EXERCISE STRESS: Both forms of angled press are isolation exercises. *Incline presses* stress the upper pectorals, front deltoids and triceps. *Decline presses* stress the lower pectorals, triceps and, to some extent, the lats.

What To Do
a. *Incline Press*
Load up the bar on the rack with rather less weight than you would use for a flat bench press. Lie on the inclined bench with your spotter behind you. With her help, lift the weight off the rack and lock out your arms at shoulder level. Lower the weight to your upper chest, then press it upwards. Repeat.

b. *Decline Press*
Load up the bar on the rack. Lie on the bench with your head downwards and with your feet hooked into the toe bar. Your spotter should be behind your head to hand you the bar from the rack. Lock out your arms. Lower the bar to your lower chest and then press it back up. Repeat.

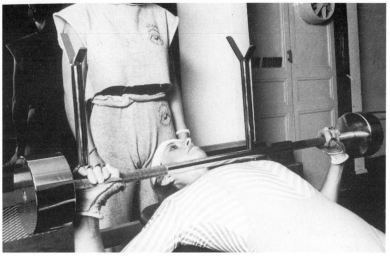
Incline Bench Presses (a)

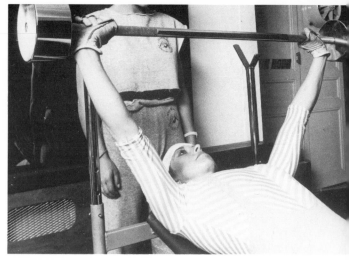
(b)

Decline Bench Presses (a)

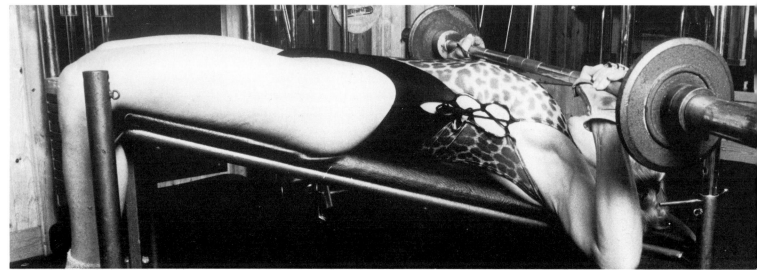

(b)

Exercise Variations

The variations on this particular theme are endless. You can vary the angle of the bench itself, you can change your grip from wide to narrow; or you can perform the exercise with dumb-bells instead of a barbell. All these variations will alter the area stressed to some extent, encouraging more complete development.

Decline presses are not, in my view, so important for women since the area stressed (the lower pecs), is always hidden by the bikini top.

Dumb-Bell Bench Presses

Any type of bench press, whether flat, incline or decline, can be performed with dumb-bells rather than a barbell. There are two advantages which apply in the case of any exercise performed with dumb-bells.

1 If you have uneven development, it will enable you to correct your proportions.
2 The exercise is very specific and stresses the muscles involved directly. This has the effect of improving definition. For this reason, dumb-bell exercises are used preferentially by bodybuilders during a pre-contest phase.

A disadvantage is the increased demand for good coordination and the fact that you cannot use as much weight as you would with a barbell bench press.

What To Do

Take up the bench press starting position. Lying on a bench, grasp a weight in each hand (a spotter can pass these to you). Lock out your arms. Keep the plates of the dumb-bells facing at right-angles to your body. Hold them at arm's length above your chest. Bend your elbows, and lower the weights down to shoulder level. Push up again, to start position. Repeat.

10. *Flat Flyes*

EXERCISE STRESS: This is the primary isolation exercise for the pectoral muscles and is an excellent means of firming up the bustline.

Flat Flyes (a)

(b)

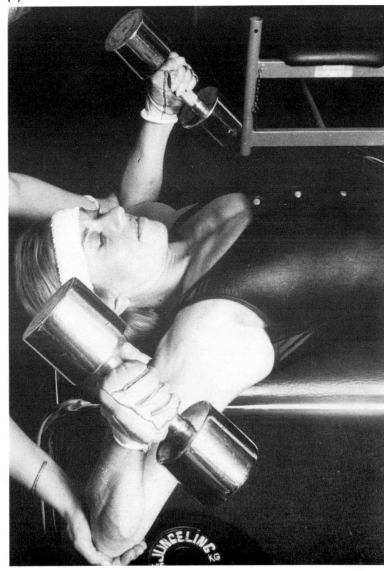

Safety Tip

It is a good idea to use a spotter for this exercise for two reasons. First of all, when the arms are fully extended, you can get stuck and be forced to drop the weights before you finish the exercise. A spotter will help you past this potential sticking point. Secondly, the weights are held above your chest and in the event of an accident could crash down on you from above.

What To Do

Take a pair of dumb-bells and lie down on a flat bench with your feet on the floor to either side. Extend your arms to hold the dumb-bells together above your chest, with your elbows bent. The plates on the dumb-bells should be pointed towards your head and feet. Concentrate on moving your elbows and forearms outwards as far as possible, until they reach below the level of the bench each side of you, and try to keep the weights facing inwards all the time. Do not let your hands stray outwards. As you extend your elbows, take a deep breath to fill your lungs and expand your chest. Feel a really good stretch in the pecs. With your elbows still bent at the same angle, push the weights back to the start position with a pincer-like movement. Do not lock

out your arms straight at the top point, keep them bent all the time.

This is not an easy exercise to perform correctly, and most people do not do it properly. The secret is to keep the elbows strictly bent at the same angle all the time, and to think of moving them and not the weights in your hands.

a. *Incline and Decline Flyes*

You can use the same angled bench for flyes as you would for bench press variations. The bench should normally be adjusted to an angle of 45°, but it can be varied any way you prefer.

EXERCISE STRESS: Incline flyes isolate the upper pectorals and front deltoids. Decline flyes work on the lower pecs.

The areas under stress are the same as those for the bench press variations, so obviously your schedule ought not to include both types of exercise at the same time. You could include incline bench press plus flat flyes, or flat bench press plus decline flyes.

What To Do

Perform the exercises in the same position as the

Incline Flyes (a)

(b)

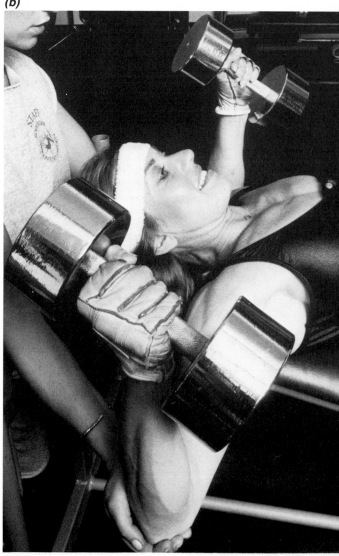

Pec. Deck Flyes (a)   *(b)*

incline and decline bench press, using the same basic movement as the flat flye. Use slightly lighter dumb-bells than you would for flat flyes, and be sure to have a spotter standing behind you.

b. *Pec. Deck Flyes*

The pec. deck machine is invaluable for working the entire pectoral area, but especially stresses the inner edges and means you will develop a great cleavage. This machine is a standard piece of equipment in most gyms.

What To Do

Select and pre-set the weight you require and adjust the seat of the machine to suit your height. Sit in the seat and rest your forearms or palms, with elbows up, against the pads to either side of you. Press them inwards until they touch in front of your chest. Concentrate on using your chest muscles rather than arm strength to bring about this movement. Hold the contraction, then slowly release the tension and return to start position. Don't let your arms relax entirely. Start the second rep while still a little tense and continue in this way throughout the set.

A training partner can help towards the end of your set by assisting the squeezing movement of the pads when you can no longer force them together in the middle on your own. This will enable you to

benefit from the negative part of the exercise or to perform a couple of forced reps.

Tip

The Nautilus pec. deck machine is particularly good if you have access to one. The stress is even throughout the fullest range of movement possible and it is a real pleasure to use.

11. *Parallel Bar Dips*

EXERCISE STRESS: The lower and outer areas of the pectoral muscles, with secondary stress on the front deltoids and triceps.

What To Do

Jump up to grasp a pair of parallel bars with your palms facing inwards. Lock out your arms straight to support yourself. Bend your legs behind you, crossing them at the ankles, and lean forward slightly at the same time.

Now bend your arms and lower your body down between the bars, as far as you can. Try to go low enough to make a 90° angle at your elbow. Push back up by straightening your arms again. Repeat.

Tips

To increase stress on the triceps, rather than the

Parallel Bar Dips (a)

(b)

pectorals, keep your body upright and do not lean forward.

Once you can perform the desired number of reps easily you can add weight by using a specially designed dip belt.

12. *Cross-Bench Pull-Overs*

EXERCISE STRESS: This exercise is excellent for expanding the rib-cage and giving depth to the chest. Many women look reasonably broad-shouldered and strong from the front or back,

Cross-Bench Pull-Overs (a)

(b)

but narrow and frail from the side. This exercise will help to correct that. The exercise primarily works the pectoral muscles, with some involvement of the lats. It also develops the serratus muscles, which are the finger-like small muscles at the top of the ribs, alongside the breasts. These always look particularly impressive when displayed in a contest.

Safety Tip
Use a spotter for this exercise. It enables you to handle more weight, and any exercise which involves handling a weight over your face is particularly risky to perform alone.

What To Do
Select a heavy flat bench, which will not overturn, or rest a barbell against one end of a bench to hold it down. Lie down with your centre back across the width of the bench with your head hanging off the edge. Your feet should be flat on the floor in front of you, legs and feet apart and your bottom well down to balance you. Get your spotter to give you a suitable dumb-bell. Take hold of it with your arms locked out above your chest. Rest both hands against the upper plate of the dumb-bell, holding it vertically, and grasp it firmly around the bar with your thumbs. The hand position is actually irrelevant, as long as you feel safe and comfortable. Now lower the weight, with slightly bent arms, backwards as far as you can. Try to reach the floor behind you. This may be impossible at first, but you will quickly gain flexibility. As you lower the weight, inhale and expand your chest. The spotter can give the weight a push up at the bottom of the movement if you get stuck. Raise the dumb-bell back up to the start position, above your chest. Lock out your arms. Exhale as you lift and make the effort.

Tips
Always keep your bottom really low throughout and never arch your back. By doing so, you will take stress away from your chest. The amount of weight used is not important and should not be so heavy that you cannot get a full stretch.

Exercise Variation: Barbell Pull-Overs
Lie flat on a bench lengthways and get your spotter to hand you a light barbell. Take it with arms locked out above your chest, with as wide a grip as possible to ensure a maximum stretch of the rib-cage. With straight arms, lower the bar behind your head as far as you can, then return the bar to the start position. Repeat.

This exercise stresses the same muscles as the cross-bench pull-over, and it is a matter of individual taste which one you prefer to choose.

UPPER BACK EXERCISES (LATISSIMUS DORSI, TRAPEZIUS)

13. *Bentover Rowing*

This is the fundamental basic exercise for building mass in the upper back.

EXERCISE STRESS: The *latissimus dorsi* muscles, *erector spinae* and arm flexors.

What To Do
Select a relatively heavy barbell. The muscles of the upper back are strong and need a lot of work. Squat down with your feet tucked well underneath the bar, shoulder-width apart. Grasp the bar with an overhand grip to either side of your feet. Keeping your back flat, chin up and bottom down, stand up, concentrating on lifting with your thigh muscles and not your arms.

Stand up straight, holding the barbell across your thighs. Now lean forward, with a flat back and with your chin up. Let the bar hang straight down in a natural position. Bend your knees slightly to take stress off your back. Pull the bar upwards and slightly back in to your waist. Concentrate on keeping your elbows as high as possible. Lower the weight slowly and under control, fighting gravity, back to the start position. Repeat.

Safety Tips
You must keep your back flat all the time. If you arch it, you could cause lower back injury. If you cannot perform the exercise without cheating in this way, reduce the weight.

To put the weight down safely, stand up straight at the end of the set, with the weight across your thighs, squat down with bent legs and replace the weight in the start position. *Never* put the weight on the floor from the mid-exercise position with a bent back. You could cause serious injury by placing heavy stress on the lower spine.

Bentover Rowing (a)

(b)

(c)

(d)

14. *Seated Pulley Rows*

EXERCISE STRESS: This is a marvellous exercise for increasing the width of the back by working the *latissimus dorsi* muscles. It also affects the centre of the upper back and middle of the back, building depth in the trapezius and *erector spinae* muscle groups.

What To Do

This exercise takes a while to set up. Select a machine with a floor pulley and attach two triangle handles to the cable. The normal foot bars will usually be too close for your purposes, so position a large plate, or pair of large flat-ended dumb-bells lengthways against them. Rest your feet against this 'extension'. Select a weight on the stack and adjust the pin. Stretch forward and grasp the handles. You should be doubled right over, with your hands and feet level. Pull the handles in to your waist, sitting up as you do so. Keep your back straight and pull your elbows as far back as you can. Let the cable pull you forward to the start position as slowly as possible. Fight it all the way. Stretch as far as you can, pulling out your lats under resistance. Hold the maximum extension for a count of one, then pull back on the cable again. Repeat.

Safety Tips

Keep your legs slightly bent throughout to take stress off your lower back. Keep your back really straight at the top of the movement and do not lean back or slump forward.

15. *Lat. Pulldowns (Behind Neck)*

EXERCISE STRESS: This exercise is mainly for the *latissimus dorsi* muscles, although incidentally it will involve the forearms, biceps and shoulders.

What To Do

The lat. pulldown machine is widely available in most gyms, as it is a basic piece of equipment.

Select a long curved bar and attach it to the overhead cable. Adjust the pin on the weight stack to your level. You can either sit on the seat provided or remove it and kneel on the floor facing the machine. If you are using heavy weights, a spotter can hold you down by grasping you around the waist from behind or putting light pressure between your shoulderblades.

Take hold of the bar above your head with an overhand grip about 6 inches wider on each side than your shoulders. Pull the bar down as far as you can behind your neck. Try to touch the base of your neck with the bar. A spotter can push the bar down that extra inch if necessary, so that you can benefit from the full range of the upward movement. Hold the peak contraction position, then let the cable pull the bar up slowly, resisting it all the way. Let it pull you right up, until you achieve maximum stretch in the lats. Repeat.

Seated Pulley Rows (a)

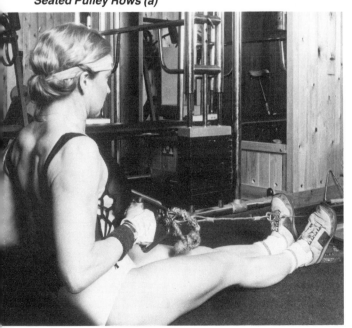

(b)

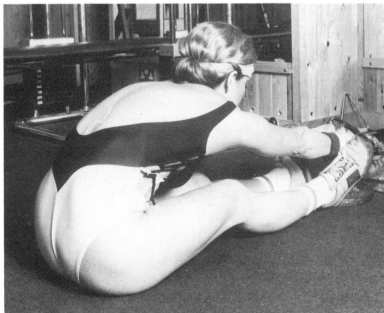

Rear Lat. Pulldowns (a)

(b)

Front Lat. Pulldowns (a)

(b)

Exercise Variations: Front Lat. Pulldowns
You can change the exercise by pulling the bar down to the chest rather than behind the neck, thereby altering the area stressed.

The handgrip can be varied from wide to narrow, anywhere along the bar. This will affect different parts of the upper back.

16. *Single Arm Dumb-Bell Rows*

EXERCISE STRESS: This exercise is mainly for the *latissimus dorsi*, but also involves the arm muscle groups (deltoids and trapezius). This is a really good exercise for building width and thickness into the lats. It stresses the whole length of the muscle as far as the waist.

What To Do
Choose a heavy dumb-bell. Stand next to a flat bench, and rest your right knee on top of it, taking your weight on your left foot. Bend forwards with a flat back and grasp the dumb-bell at floor level in your left hand with your arm straight. Rest your right hand lightly on the bench top to support yourself. Bend your arm and pull the weight up to waist level, concentrate on getting your elbow as high as possible and keep the back horizontal. Keep your chin up. Lower the weight as slowly as possible back to the start position, resisting gravity. Feel a good stretch in the lat. muscle at maximum extension. Repeat first one side, then change over and work the other side, using the same number of reps.

17. *Chins*

EXERCISE STRESS: Another really excellent exercise for increasing your upper back width by working the lats, and also involving the arms.

What To Do
Most gyms have a high-level chinning bar, often as an integral part of a multigym machine. You can also buy quite cheaply a bar to fit into a doorway at home. Hang from the bar with your hands shoulder-width apart. You can use an overhand or underhand grip, though undergrasp is a little easier. Pull yourself up to the bar and hold the position. Lower yourself slowly and repeat.

Single Arm Dumb-Bell Rows (a)

(b)

Chins (a)

(b)

Tips

This is at first a tough exercise for women to perform. The weak link in the chain, usually your arm flexor muscles, will give up first. You may need to start by performing only the downward movement from the top, by getting a spotter to lift you up. (Cross your ankles so that the spotter can push you up by the feet.) Most women will take some time to develop sufficient strength to perform many reps of chins. It is very galling to watch novice male bodybuilders walk in the gym and perform ten or so chins straight off, due to their extra natural upper body muscle strength, but perseverance will win for you in the end.

18. *Upright Rows*

EXERCISE STRESS: This is an important basic exercise for building strength and size in the upper back and shoulders. The muscles affected are the trapezius, deltoids and, to a lesser extent, the arm muscles.

What To Do
Start with your feet under the bar, approximately 12 inches apart. Squat down and take hold of the bar with an overhand grip, hands no more than 6 inches apart. Stand up, using your thigh muscles, keeping your back flat, chin up and bottom down. Stand erect with the bar held at arm's length across your front

Upright Rows (a)

thighs. Now pull the bar up slowly to chin level or as high as possible. The bar should be held under your chin, but should not be in contact with your chest. Hold it an inch or two away from your body throughout the lift. Now lower the bar slowly and under control back to the starting point. Repeat.

SHOULDER EXERCISES (DELTOIDS, TRAPEZIUS)

19. *Seated Presses Behind Neck*

EXERCISE STRESS: This is an excellent all-round shoulder exercise for building strength and size. It

Seated Presses Behind Neck (a)

(b)

works the whole of the deltoid muscle, especially the front part, as well as the trapezius muscle and the arms.

What To Do
Adjust the top of an exercise bench to the vertical position and pin it in place. Sit on the end of the bench, leaning against the upright support and ask

(b)

your spotter to hand you a barbell of suitable weight from behind. Receive the bar with arms locked out, and your hands shoulder-width apart. Your spotter should stand closely behind you throughout the exercise.

Slowly lower the bar under control down to the shoulders. Go down as low as you can reach, then push straight back up again. If you fail at the bottom of the movement, your spotter can give you slight assistance to help you past the 'sticking point'. Repeat.

Variations

You can do this exercise standing up, or with various different hand-grip widths. If you try the standing version, use a power-clean to raise the barbell from the floor to your chest and into the starting position.

20. *Military Presses*

EXERCISE STRESS: This exercise affects much the same muscles as the behind neck press – the front deltoids and trapezius – but also the chest, and therefore you should not include both exercises in one programme.

What To Do

Select a suitable barbell and stand with your legs about 12 inches or so apart, then power-clean it up to your chest. From this position, press the barbell overhead until your arms lock out. Make sure the weight is pressed directly upwards and does not stray either forwards or backwards, thereby involving incorrect muscle groups. Lower the bar back to your chest slowly and deliberately. Repeat.

Tips

The upward press should be a moderately 'explosive' movement. If you try to do it slowly, you will probably get stuck.

A spotter should stand behind you throughout this exercise.

Military Presses (a)

(b)

Seated Dumb-Bell Shoulder Presses (a)   **(b)**

Safety Tip
As with all standing exercises, do not lean
backwards. Keep your back straight and the
muscles tight throughout. If you are tempted to
cheat, use a lighter weight.

21. *Seated Dumb-Bell Shoulder Presses*

EXERCISE STRESS: This is an exercise for the front
deltoids, upper chest and arms. It is a good idea to
use dumb-bells if you have uneven arm or shoulder
development, since they will help to equalize it and
correct the fault in your symmetry.

What To Do
Adjust a bench top as for the press-behind-neck
exercise. Sit on the end of the bench, leaning against

the support. Take a pair of dumb-bells and hold
them with your arms bent to each side of your chest,
with the bars facing forwards. Inhale, then firmly
press the dumb-bells upwards together until they
are over your head. Keep your arms slightly bent
and under tension throughout the exercise. Do not
lock out at the top of the press. Slowly lower the
weights again. Repeat.

Safety Tip
A spotter should be handy for this exercise, since
you are particularly vulnerable when the
dumb-bells are held overhead.

Exercise Variations
You can do this exercise standing up but be careful
not to lean backwards. The dumb-bells can be
pressed overhead alternately. This allows your

Shrugs (a)

(b)

brain to concentrate on coordinating the move individually and you may find you can use more weight as a result.

Dumb-bell shoulder presses can also be performed on an incline bench, to vary the angle at which you hit the deltoids.

22. *Shrugs*

EXERCISE STRESS: Shrugs directly affect the trapezius muscles. They are the best exercise to perform if you have poor posture. Rounded shoulders can be caused by the stretching of the trapezius muscles, and consequent shortening of the pectorals. Shrugs will tighten up the traps, whereas flyes will help the pecs.

What To Do
Select a suitable barbell. Lift it up from a squat position using your legs, and hold it with your arms hanging down to either side of you. Lift your shoulders as high as you can, trying to reach your ears, then press them back as far as you can and then downwards. Bring the shoulders forward, back to the start position, and repeat.

Variations
You can perform this exercise by holding dumb-bells across your thighs in a standing position.

You can also use the bench press station of a multigym machine. Remove the bench, and stand in between the metal arms. Keeping your arms straight, hold on to the machine and shrug up, back and down as you would with dumb-bells. You can adjust the weight stack on the machine to suit your strength.

23. *Front Lateral Raises*

EXERCISE STRESS: This is an isolation exercise for the front deltoids and should be used in combination with the side lateral raise and rear lateral raise (described below, pp. 67, 68).

What To Do
Take a pair of light dumb-bells. Position yourself in front of a mirror and stand upright with your feet comfortably apart, and with your arms hanging down straight to either side of you, holding the dumb-bells. The bar of the dumb-bells should face forwards, with your palms to the rear. Raise one of your extended arms slowly and under control, being

sure to maintain a straight-arm position, until the weight is level with your shoulder. Hold the position, then lower the arm slowly, fighting gravity. Repeat the movement with your other arm. Repeat, using alternate arms.

Variations
This exercise can be performed with a barbell held in front of you with both hands, shoulder-width apart, though there is an extra problem to contend with in coordinating balance in this variation.

24. *Side Lateral Raises*

EXERCISE STRESS: This is an isolation exercise for the middle of the deltoid muscle, which forms a 'cap' to the shoulder. The exercise can be performed alone, but is best done in combination with the front and rear lateral raises, which will develop all three areas of the deltoid evenly.

a. *Method 1: Standing Side Lateral Raise*
What To Do
You will probably not be able to handle very much weight for this exercise, so choose a pair of light dumb-bells. Hold the dumb-bells in front of your

thighs end-on with your palms facing each other. Bend your elbows slightly. Now slowly raise your arms out to your sides and upwards, until they reach approximately as far as your shoulders. Rotate the dumb-bells as you lift by twisting your wrists inwards, so that the bars face forwards at the top point. Hold the contraction, then slowly lower the weights back to the starting point.

Safety Tips
Make sure you maintain correct form throughout. Do not swing your torso backwards from the hips, thereby using your back muscles to help you lift. Stay firmly upright and use only your shoulder muscles.

b. *Method 2: Seated Lateral Raises*
What To Do
Sit astride a flat exercise bench. Hold a light dumb-bell in each hand, hanging down by your sides. Keeping your back upright, slowly raise the dumb-bells out to each side until they reach shoulder-level. Twist your wrists inwards at the top to rotate the weights slightly. Keep your elbows bent throughout. Hold, then, as slowly as you can, lower your arms back to the start position. Repeat.

Front Lateral Raises (a)

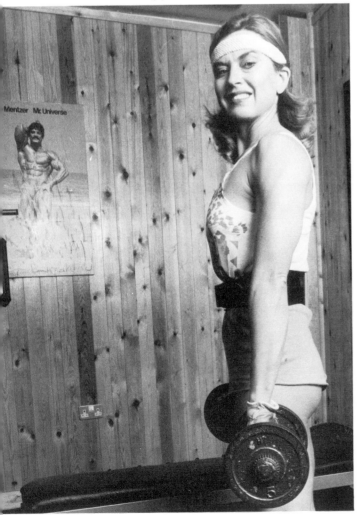

(b)

Side Lateral Raises (a)

(b)

Variations
Either standing or seated lateral raises can be
performed with a dumb-bell, one arm at a time. If
you are standing, hold on to a piece of equipment
with your free hand.

c. *Method 3: Pulley Side Laterals*
What To Do
You can use a cable attached to the floor pulley on a
machine to perform single arm side laterals.
Standing sideways on to the machine, take the
handle in the hand which is furthest from the
machine, so that the cable stretches across your
body. If it happens to be your right hand, start with
it in front of your left thigh. Keeping your elbow

bent, pull the cable across your body, and up to
shoulder-level on the right side of you. Allow the
cable to pull your arm back down to the start
position as slowly as you can. Repeat and then
perform on the opposite side of your body.

25. *Rear Lateral Raises*

EXERCISE STRESS: This is the third in the trio of
specific isolation exercises for the deltoids and this
one stresses the rear portion of the muscle group.

a. *Method 1: Standing Bent Laterals*
What To Do
Select two light dumb-bells. Holding one in each

Rear Lateral Raises (a)

(b)

hand, stand with your feet comfortably apart and bend over with a flat back until your body is at right-angles to your legs. Let your arms hang down so that the dumb-bells are held together below your waist. Now bend your elbows slightly and lift the dumb-bells slowly out to your sides. Raise your elbows as high as you can at the top, then lower again as slowly as you can. Repeat.

b. *Method 2: Seated Rear Lateral Raises*
What To Do

Sit on the end of a flat exercise bench, with your feet about 8 inches away from the legs of the bench. Take a pair of light dumb-bells and lean right forward until your chest is resting on your knees. Hold the weights together at floor level behind your ankles. Bend your elbows slightly, and then raise the dumb-bells up and outwards to the sides of you as high as you can reach. Hold for a count of one at the top, then slowly lower back to start position. Repeat.

Tip
Keep your chest on your knees throughout and your head down. This exercise feels very awkward to perform at first, but gets easier as you gain flexibility in the shoulders.

c. *Method 3: Pulley Bent Laterals*
What To Do

Using a floor pulley on a machine, stand in the same position as for pulley side laterals. The exercise is performed in a similar fashion, except that in this instance you should bend over with a flat back as for Method 1. Place your feet shoulder-width apart in the start position, hold the handle of the pulley at knee level and pull the cable across your body to thigh-height only. Return slowly to the start position. Repeat on each side.

LOWER BACK EXERCISES

26. *Deadlifts*

EXERCISE STRESS: This mainly concentrates on the lower spinal erectors, *gluteus maximus* and quadriceps, but indirectly affects other back muscle groups, as well as the abdominals, arms and calves. This is a heavy basic exercise and together with the squat and bench press, is one of the three competitive power lifts. The exercise affects so many major muscle groups that it is a good general conditioner but it is primarily used to build strength and mass in the lower back muscles.

The spinal erector muscles take a long time to recover from stress, so this exercise should not be performed with really heavy weights more than once each week. On other back training days, alternate it with moderately weighted 'good mornings' or hyperextensions. As this exercise involves the major muscle groups of the legs and back, some of the largest in the body, you can use a lot of weight, so do not be afraid to do so. Provided that you lift in correct form you will not hurt yourself. You should wear a leather lifting belt for this exercise.

What To Do
Place a heavy barbell on the gym floor in front of you. If possible, select an area with a non-slip

Stiff-Legged Deadlifts (a)

(b)

surface, either rubber matting or wood. Put your feet well under the bar, 12 inches or so apart. Take an alternate grip (i.e. one hand over, and one hand under the bar). Your hands should be just to either side of your feet. Squat down with a flat back until your legs are just slightly above thighs, parallel. Keep your chin up.

With your arms straight, raise the bar, being sure to concentrate on lifting with your legs and not your arms. Keep the barbell as close to your thighs as possible to minimize strain on the back, and shrug back your shoulders at the top of the lift.

To lower the weight, bend your legs and squat down, still with straight arms, flat back and chin up.

Safety Tips
Wear a wide leather lifting belt to perform this exercise. Keep a flat back throughout. Do not arch forward when lifting or lowering the bar. Do not lean back at the top of the lift. **Always** squat down to lower the weight and **never** put it down from a bent-over position.

Keep your bottom low and your chin up when lifting with the back flat. This will help to correct the overall torso position.

27. *Stiff-Legged Deadlifts*

EXERCISE STRESS: This concentrates on the *erector spinae*, leg biceps and gluteus muscles. Although this is primarily a lower back exercise, it is also one of the best for tightening up the buttocks. Incidentally you will also get a terrific stretch in your hamstrings.

What To Do
Select a relatively heavy barbell and place it on the end of an exercise bench. Stand on top of the bench at one end by the bar, with your feet together. Bend over and take hold of the bar with an overhand grip to each side of your feet. Keeping your legs and arms absolutely straight, stand up, until the bar rests against your thighs. Slowly lower the weight back to the start position, still with straight legs, to get a really good stretch in the hamstrings. Lower the barbell as far as you can below the bench without straining. Repeat.

Safety Tips
This is definitely **not** a beginner's exercise. It is for the advanced trainer only.

If you have any lower back pain or general back problems this exercise is best avoided. Try hyperextensions or 'good mornings' instead.

This is one of the few exercises performed with straight legs. Since this contravenes a basic safety

principle, take extra care. This also applies to 'good mornings' (Exercise No. 29 below).

Variations
The exercise can be performed standing on the bench with dumb-bells. These can be lowered down below the level of the bench top to either side to get a really good stretch.

You can also perform the exercise standing with your feet on a block on the gym floor, but I think the bench method is more effective.

28. *Hyperextensions*

EXERCISE STRESS: This is for the spinal erector muscles, and, to a lesser extent, the gluteus muscles. This exercise strengthens the lower back.

What To Do
Method 1
Lie face down across a high level bench (e.g. the leg extension or leg curl machine) and ask your spotter to hold on to your feet. Balance on the bench, so your upper body is completely free on one side, supported by your hips. Place your hands behind your head, and then bend your upper body forwards, until your head is almost touching the floor. Slowly come back up again, keeping your head up and back flat, until you are arched slightly backwards. Hold this contracted position briefly then repeat the forward movement. Repeat. As your back becomes stronger, hold a small barbell plate (say 2½ kilos) behind your head and gradually build up the weight you use.

Method 2
If your gym has a hyperextension machine you will not need a training partner to assist you. Lean forward across the waist-level pad and hook your toes into the retaining rungs to the rear. Perform the exercise just as you would for Method 1.

29. *'Good Mornings'*

EXERCISE STRESS: An alternative exercise choice for the *erector spinae* and leg bicep muscles. (No one can tell me why this exercise is called a 'good morning'!)

What To Do
Stand upright with your feet in a comfortable position, and with a fairly light barbell held across your shoulders. Keeping your legs straight, bend forward with a flat back until your trunk is at right angles to your legs. Try to get your shoulders as low as you can. Keep your chin up throughout. Slowly stand upright and return to the start position.

Hyperextensions (a)

(b)

Good Mornings (a)

(b)

Safety Tip
This exercise is one of the very few performed with stiff legs, in contravention of a basic safety rule, so be extra careful when performing it.

ARM EXERCISES: (i) THE BICEPS

30. *Barbell Curls*

EXERCISE STRESS: Concentrating on the muscles at the front of the upper arm (the biceps and brachialis), as well as the inside of the forearms, this is the most important basic heavy exercise for building strength and mass in the biceps. It is an essential exercise for women, who are usually under-developed in this area. Good biceps and triceps will give you curvaceous shapely arms, and you should never be afraid of building them up.

What To Do
Stand with your feet comfortably apart and a suitable barbell on the floor in front of you. With a shoulder-width underhand grip lift the bar to rest across your thighs. Tuck your elbows in to your waist, and hold them there throughout the exercise.

Now slowly curl the bar up to your shoulders. Keep your wrists rigid and do not bend them inwards at the top of the lift. This will take stress off the biceps muscle. Hold the peak contraction, flexing hard, then slowly lower the bar back to the start position, fighting gravity all the way. Repeat.

Safety Tips
Do not lean back to help you lift or press your elbows against your body. This is unsafe and also cheats you of the maximum benefit of the exercise, since the back muscles will become involved and take stress from the biceps. Reduce the amount of weight you use if you cannot perform the exercise in strict form on your own. A spotter can help by standing in front of you and slightly assisting the lift at the bottom of the movement, to help you past the sticking point. You can lean against a wall to help prevent yourself cheating, or wear the specially designed barbell curl harness around your neck, which will be available in some gyms.

Variations
a. *Standing Dumb-Bell Curls*
The standing bicep curl exercise can be performed using dumb-bells instead of a barbell. The stress is exactly the same, but the advantage of using dumb-bells is that if you have one arm weaker or smaller than the other, they will eventually be equalized. It is also possible to exercise the muscles more fully by twisting the wrists as you curl.

What To Do
The exercise is performed in exactly the same way as barbell curls. Hold a pair of dumb-bells with an underhand grip to either side of your thighs, with their plates at right angles to your body. Curl them up to your shoulders, either both together, or one after the other in a continuous motion, until the set is complete.

Barbell Curls (a)

(b)

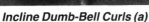
Incline Dumb-Bell Curls (a)

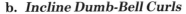
(b)

b. *Incline Dumb-Bell Curls*
Incline Dumb-Bell Curls can be performed on a bench inclined at 45°. This is a good basic building exercise.

What To Do
Lie back with your head flat against the incline board holding a dumb-bell at arm's length. Your arms should be hanging straight down to either side of the bench. Now curl the weights up to your shoulders. As you lift, rotate your wrists outwards, so that the bicep is worked not only in a straight up and down motion, but also in a twisting manner. The bicep is used for both movements in everyday life, so it should be stressed in each way whenever possible.

Flex the bicep at the top of the lift, hold, then lower as slowly as you can until the arms are hanging straight by the bench side again. Repeat.

31. *Preacher Curls*

EXERCISE STRESS: This is an exercise for the biceps, particularly the lower end which attaches at the inside of the elbows. The forearms and brachialis are also stressed.

What To Do
Some gyms will be equipped with a specially designed preacher bench, but you can perform this exercise by sitting behind the back of an ordinary inclined bench and leaning over it.

Run your forearms down the inclined bench, and ask your spotter to hand you a suitable barbell when your arms are locked out. Then slowly curl the bar up towards your chest. Flex hard at the top, keeping your wrists straight. Lower the barbell slowly back down to the start position. Repeat.

Tips
A spotter can be positioned in front of you to help you lift at the lowest point, if you need assistance. At this moment, you will be stressing the muscle at full extension – a very weak area. As you curl upwards, it will become much easier to lift as you involve the central part of the muscle, which is strong and better developed in comparison.

One of the great advantages of the Nautilus Curl Machine is that stress is equalized throughout the full range of movement, thereby eliminating the unevenness of a free weight curl. If you have access to a Nautilus machine, this is one exercise I would thoroughly recommend you should include in your programme, either as well as, or instead of, free weight curls.

Preacher Curls (a)

(b)

32. *Concentration Curls*

EXERCISE STRESS: Concentrating on the biceps, forearms, this is an isolation exercise for adding a 'peak' to the biceps. As such, it is a 'finishing detail' exercise suitable for pre-competition schedules, rather than heavy off-season bulking work. Do not make the common mistake of trying to add a 'peak' to nothing at all! You have to have muscle bulk first, developed by means of heavy basic exercises.

What To Do
Sit on the side of a bench with your legs apart. Take a dumb-bell in your right hand, lean forward and hold the dumb-bell at arm's length (floor level), with your elbow resting against the inside of your right knee. Support yourself by placing your left hand on your left knee. The plates of the dumb-bell should be facing to the front and back of you, and your wrist should be turned towards your left leg. Curl the dumb-bell up towards your chin, bracing your elbow against your knee. Flex hard at the top, then lower

very slowly back to the start position until your arm is quite straight. Repeat with alternate arms.

Tip
If you find your arm failing after a couple of sets, be your own spotter by supporting your wrist slightly at the bottom of the lift to help it past the sticking point. Don't cheat!

33. *Cable or Pulley Curls*

EXERCISE STRESS: This is an exercise for the biceps and forearms.

What To Do
Attach a triangle handle to the floor pulley of a machine. Adjust the weight stack. Stand facing the machine and some way back from it. From an extended arm position, curl the pulley handle up towards your shoulder. Stand firmly upright throughout and do not lean backwards. Flex hard,

Concentration Curls (a) (b)

Cable Curls (a) (b)

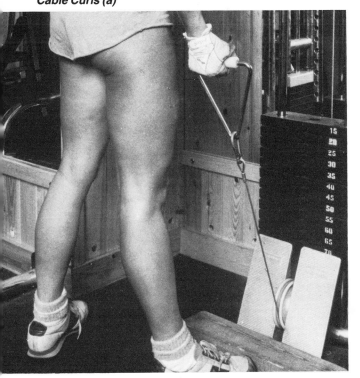 

then allow the cable to pull your arm slowly back to the start position. Repeat with alternate arms.

Tip
Keep your elbows tucked in to your waist throughout this exercise, or you will lose stress on the biceps.

out, directly above your chest. Grip the bar in the centre, with your hands no more than a hand's breadth apart. Lower the bar slowly backwards towards your forehead. Touch your hairline with the bar, then press it straight back up again.

Keep your upper arms vertical throughout this

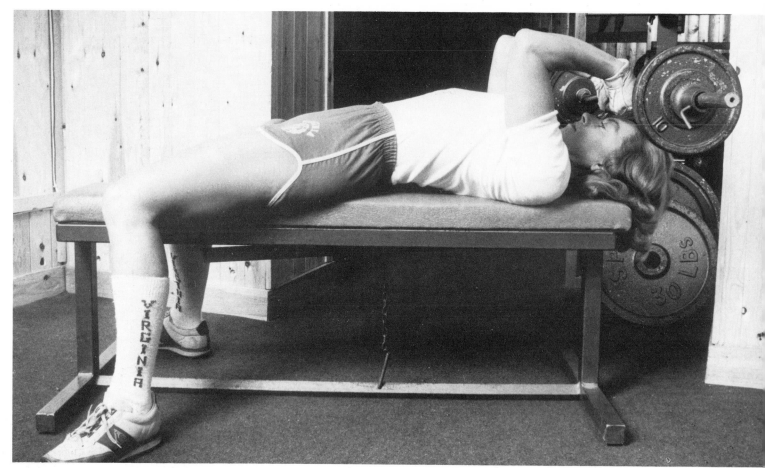

Lying Triceps Extensions (a)

(b)

ARM EXERCISES: (ii) THE TRICEPS

As the triceps is, by definition, a muscle divided into three parts, you will need to include an exercise for each 'head' of the triceps in your schedule to achieve all-round symmetrical development.

34. *Lying Triceps Extensions*

EXERCISE STRESS: This is the most basic exercise for the triceps, and a fundamental mass-builder. It particularly stresses the inner head of the muscle.

What To Do
Lie supine on an exercise bench, with your head towards one end, but not hanging off the edge. Ask your spotter to pass you a light bar from behind your head and receive it with your arms locked straight

exercise so that only your forearms move up and down, and keep pressing your elbows inwards all the time. This will isolate stress on the triceps. You should feel this intensely.

Safety Tips

Do not perform this exercise without a spotter. As the barbell is lowered across your face, using a generally weak muscle, it is obviously hazardous. You can easily fail to lift the weight from above your forehead. Spotters can help at this point with slight assistance in lifting.

The spotter should always hand over, and take away the bar from behind the exerciser's head. If you are the exerciser, **always** hold on to the bar together with the spotter until it is safely away from your face, regardless of your spotter's experience.

Variations

Lying triceps extensions can also be performed on an incline or decline bench to vary the angle of stress on the muscle.

35. *Triceps Extensions Behind Neck*

EXERCISE STRESS: This exercise stresses the whole triceps muscle, but particularly the large inner head.

What To Do

Adjust the seat of an exercise bench to the upright position and sit on the end, leaning against it to

support your back. Ask a spotter to stand behind and pass you a barbell. Receive the bar with your arms locked out straight above your head, and take a narrow underhand grip, with your hands no more than 4 to 6 inches apart.

Keeping your upper arms extended, lower the barbell slowly behind your head as low as you can, towards your shoulders. Now push the bar forcefully back up to the start position, until your arms lock out straight. Press your elbows inwards throughout the exercise. Repeat.

Tips

You will discover that if you perform this exercise really strictly, you will be unable to use much weight. A spotter can help you by assisting with the lift at the back of the neck, where your leverage is weakest.

Variations

This exercise can be performed standing up, with a barbell, or with a dumb-bell as follows:

Single Arm Triceps Extension Behind Neck

Stand in front of a mirror holding a light dumb-bell in your right hand. Press the weight overhead until your arm is locked out straight above your right shoulder. Keep your upper arm pressed against your right ear throughout the exercise. Steady your right arm by stretching your left arm diagonally across behind your head and grasping the back of your

Triceps Extensions Behind Neck (a)

(b)

Single Arm Triceps Extensions Behind Neck (a) (b)

right elbow. Now lower the dumb-bell across behind your head towards your opposite shoulder. Feel a good stretch, then press the dumb-bell diagonally back upright to the start position. Lock out your arms. Repeat with one arm, then the other.

36. *Close-Grip Bench Presses*

EXERCISE STRESS: This is a good general mass-builder for the inner 'head' of the triceps and pectorals.

What To Do
Follow the instructions as directed for the bench press (Exercise 8), but take a narrow underhand grip, with your hands no more than 6 inches apart.

Safety Tip
As for all bench press variations, **never** perform this movement without a spotter, however experienced you may be. A champion woman powerlifter in Canada recently choked to death pinned under a barbell while training alone in her basement gym at home.

37. *Pulley Pushdowns*

EXERCISE STRESS: Pushdowns work the entire triceps muscle, but particularly the outer 'head'.

What To Do
Attach a short straight bar to the overhead pulley of an exercise machine. Adjust the pin in the weight stack to a suitable level. Stand facing the machine with your feet comfortably apart and fairly close to it. Grasp the bar above you and pull it right down to your thighs, locking out your arms. Tuck your elbows tightly against your sides. Now let the cable pull the bar slowly upwards, until it reaches chest level, then push down hard until your arms lock out again.

Tips
The stress is very specific in this exercise and you should really feel the triceps working. Do not cheat. Reduce the amount of weight you are using if you are tempted to lean back or let your elbows stray outwards. A spotter can give you a little help at the top of the movement if necessary.

Pulley Pushdowns (a)

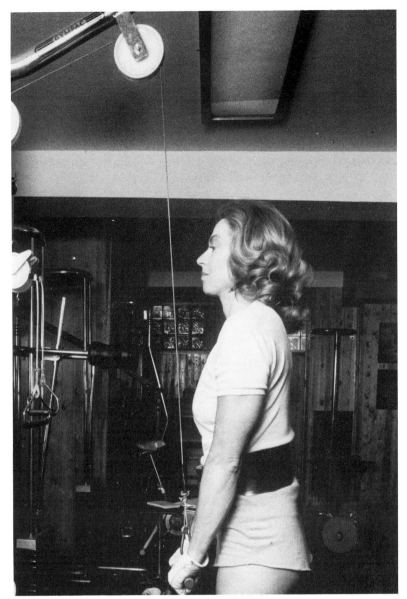

(b)

Variation
Reverse Triceps Pushdown
A most effective variation is to perform this exercise while standing on a bench with your back to the machine. Attach the long lat. pull-down bar to the overhead cable. Grasp the bar behind your waist with a close grip. (A spotter can pull it down into the start position for you.) Let the cable pull the handle up slowly until it reaches the centre of your back, then push it down forcefully until your arms lock out. Keep your elbows tucked in throughout the exercise. Repeat.

Tips
You can use a lot more weight for this variation of pulley pushdowns and it always gives a terrific 'pump' in the muscle. I always do this exercise last in my work-out, because it is very strenuous and totally wipes out my arms.

38. *Tricep Dips Between Benches*

EXERCISE STRESS: This is for the triceps, front deltoids and pectorals. It is often used by bodybuilders to give a really good final 'pump' to the triceps at the end of a training session.

What To Do
Arrange two flat exercise benches, with their long sides parallel to one another and your leg length apart. Lean against one bench, supporting yourself with your arms locked out behind you. Now raise up your legs until your feet are resting on the edge of the other bench opposite you. Bend your arms and slowly lower your bottom down towards the floor, keeping your feet on the bench. Hold your body rigid and do not sag in the middle. Get your seat down as low as you can. Now straighten your arms and return your body to the start position. Repeat.

Tricep Dips Between Benches (a)

(b)

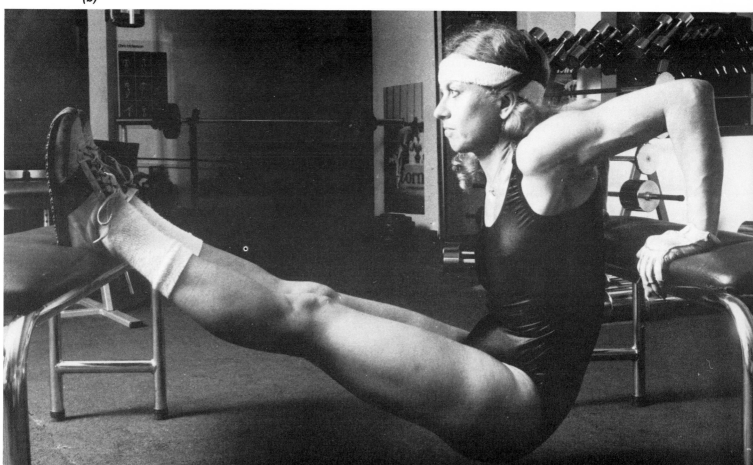

Triceps Kick-Backs (a)

(b)

Tips
This is a tough exercise and not really for the beginner. Gradually progress to a lower position and more reps. Always perform this exercise to failure, so you cannot manage another rep.

As you get stronger you can add a light barbell plate, balanced on your stomach to increase stress.

39. *Triceps Kick-Backs*

EXERCISE STRESS: This is an isolation exercise for the triceps, and the best method for exerting a peak contraction effect.

What To Do
Hold a light dumb-bell in your right hand. Bend over with a straight back until your body and legs are at right-angles. Place your left leg forwards to balance yourself and support yourself with your left hand holding on to your left knee.

Bend your right arm holding the dumb-bell, keeping your upper arm tightly pressed against your side. Now straighten your arm, pushing it up and back as far as you can. Return slowly to start position. Repeat with one arm then the other.

ARM EXERCISES: (iii) FOREARMS

For beginners, the wrists are often a really weak link and make lifting and coordination unnecessarily hard. Wrist exercises are mainly useful for initially increasing the strength of the tendons and ligaments around the joints, to aid you in lifting during most other exercises. I would recommend including wrist curls only in your early programmes. The wrists will always get a lot of incidental work in every work-out, without doing any special exercises for them later.

I don't consider forearm exercises of prime importance for women in terms of building muscle bulk. Bulky forearms are really only needed by male bodybuilders, to counterbalance the massive muscularity they tend to build very rapidly in their upper arms. Few women are likely to have this symmetry problem.

40. *Reverse Curls*

EXERCISE STRESS: This concentrates on the arm flexors, biceps, brachialis.

81

Reverse Curls (a)

(b)

Wrist Curls (a)

(b)

What To Do

Select a barbell of moderate weight. Stand up, holding the bar across your thighs. Tuck your elbows into your waist and keep them there throughout the exercise. Bend your arms and slowly lift the bar up towards your shoulders. Slowly lower the bar back to start position. Repeat.

41. *Wrist Curls*

EXERCISE STRESS: The muscles of the inside of the forearm (flexors).

What To Do

Kneel down facing the long side of an exercise bench, with your forearms facing upwards across the width of the bench. Let your hands and wrists hang

over the edge. Keep your forearms close together all along their length, from the elbows to the hands. Ask your spotter to give you a suitable barbell. Take hold of it with an underhand close grip. Your hands should actually touch. Now slowly curl the bar upwards as far as you can, flexing your inner forearm as you do so. Hold the contraction briefly, then slowly lower the bar. Allow your fingers to uncurl slightly and run the bar down their length, then close your grip and curl the hands back up again to the top. Repeat.

Tip

Your spotter should kneel in front of you, on the opposite side of the bench, to balance the bar. If you try to hold it steady yourself, you will have trouble performing the exercise in strict form.

Variation

You can also perform this exercise by sitting on the bench, with your legs together, and positioning your parallel forearms along your thighs, pressed tightly together from the elbow to wrist. Let your hands hang down over your knees. Grasp the bar in both hands with a close underhand grip, bend forward over your thighs and forearms and perform the exercise as described above.

42. *Reverse Wrist Curls*

EXERCISE STRESS: Muscles at the back of the forearms (extensors).

What To Do

Assume exactly the same position as taken for either variation of the wrist curl exercises above. Use a barbell with about half the weight used for wrist curls. This time, take a close overhand grip on the bar and lift and lower in the reverse motion. Have a spotter handy to steady the bar as before. Repeat.

THE CALVES

Because the calves are in such constant use carrying your bodyweight, they need a great deal of training and are almost impossible to overload. Exercises concentrating on them should be included in your programme at least every other training session. Even a novice woman should start with a heavy weight.

43. *Standing Calf-Raises*

EXERCISE STRESS: This is an isolation exercise for the gastrocnemius muscle in the calves.

What To Do

Most well-equipped gyms will have a calf-raise machine. Adjust the pin in the weight stack to a suitably heavy weight, and also adjust the shoulder pads to suit your own height. They should be low enough for you to have to dip down slightly, with bent legs, to position your shoulders underneath them. Balance your toes on the foot block provided, with your feet touching in a parallel position and facing directly forwards. Your heels should be right off the edge of the block.

Now raise yourself up as far as you can on to your toes and straighten your legs. Keeping your legs locked straight, lower your heels down as low as you can, well below the level of the block, to get a really good stretch. Then rise up again. Continue for as

many reps as you can manage. Always work your calves until they fail.

Tips

This exercise hurts! I find it very helpful after a set of calf-raises to stretch my calves out. To do this, extend alternate legs behind you, as far as possible, in a reverse lunge movement. Press your toes into the floor and push your heel down hard. Hold the stretch until the muscle recovers and you are ready to continue.

Variations

Each time you work your calves, you should vary your foot position so that the muscle is hit from three different angles.

a. Feet together and toes facing forwards.
b. Heels together and toes wide apart.
c. Toes pointing inwards and touching, and heels wide apart.

Perform the exercise in exactly the same way each time.

If you are doing six sets of calf-raises, perform the three variations, twice each.

Barbell Calf-Raises

If your gym is not equipped with a calf-raise machine the exercise can be performed with a free weight.

First of all, take a block, at least 4 inches deep, on which you can comfortably balance, with your heels off the edge. Place a suitable barbell across your shoulders and perform the exercise as you would on the machine.

There are two main problems with this version:

1 It is not possible to use a very heavy weight.
2 It is very hard to balance.

Always use a machine if you can.

44. *Seated Calf-Raises*

EXERCISE STRESS: This is for the soleus muscle behind the gastrocnemius, which is not stressed by any other exercise.

What To Do

The seated calf-raise machine is the best way of performing this exercise but, in my experience, it is rarely available in gyms, therefore I shall only describe a method which can be performed with free weights.

Place a 4-inch wood block alongside an exercise bench. Sit on the bench and place your feet on the block, with your heels off the edge. Pad your knees thickly with a folded towel, then ask a spotter to place a heavy barbell across your knees. Grasp it

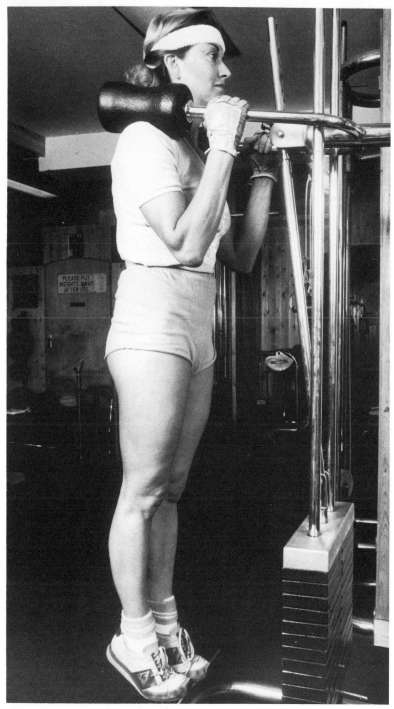

Standing Calf-Raises (a) *(b)*

firmly, using an underhand grip. Rise up on to your toes, as high as possible, then lower your heels as far as possible downwards into a full stretch position. Perform this exercise with your feet in the same three foot positions as for the standing calf-raise exercise. Work until the muscles fail on each set.

An alternative method is to have a large attractive man sit on your knees with his back to you, and grasp him around the waist. This is the most pleasant way of doing calf-raises that I know!

45. *Donkey Calf-Raises*

EXERCISE STRESS: This is particularly for the gastrocnemius muscle.

What To Do

You will need a reasonably heavy training partner to help perform this exercise.

Select a waist-level support, preferably a bar, and stand in front of it, with your feet balanced on a 4-inch wood block, toes on, heels off. Lean forward with a flat back and lightly rest your hands on the support. Do not grip it tensely. Bend your legs to allow your partner to climb up on to your back and sit astride your hips. Straighten your legs, and then perform calf-raises in the usual manner, rising up and stretching down as far as possible each time. Finish your first set, in foot position 1, then change

84

over to allow your partner his/her turn. Keep alternating in this way, until you have each performed the required number of sets in three separate toe positions.

Safety Tip
Sit well back on your partner's hips when you are in the saddle. This way the stress goes down the long bones of the legs. If you sit too far forward, you will strain your partner's lower back, and could cause injury, as well as reducing stress on the calf muscles.

ABDOMINAL EXERCISES

In theory, these should be performed at the end of your programme but I usually do them first since they are a good warm-up and because I don't like doing them and I know I would skip them if they came last. Do not, however, perform abdominal exercises prior to a leg work-out. You will need strong fresh muscles to support your back for heavy squats and deadlifts. Work your abs. at the end on these occasions.

The basic beginners' ab. exercises (leg-raises, sit-ups and twists) have already been described above (pp. 31–4). The following exercises are more advanced and you can try these when the basic exercises become too easy.

46. *Off-Bench Leg-Raises*

EXERCISE STRESS: For the lower abdomen (*rectus abdominis*).

Hanging Leg-Raises (a)

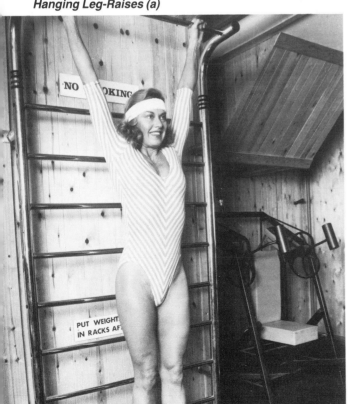

What To Do
Lie flat on an exercise bench, with your bottom right on the edge at one end. Grasp the bench each side of you above your head or at hip level, whichever you find most comfortable. Extend your legs out in front of you and bend the knees slightly. Keep them bent throughout the exercise. Now raise your legs up together until they are at right-angles to your hips, then slowly lower them back down again, until they almost touch the floor. Do not relax your abdomen at any time. Stretch your legs as far forward in this position as you can, then repeat the movement. Carry on until the muscles fail.

If you wish, you can wear ankle-weights or hold a light dumb-bell between your feet to add resistance.

Variations
Incline Leg-Raises
There are numerous variations on the leg-raise theme. To make it harder, you can try it on an inclined abdominal board. The steeper the angle of incline, the harder the exercise will be. You can do this variation either with both legs together, or alternating one at a time.

47. *Hanging Leg-Raises*

EXERCISE STRESS: The most difficult variation of all is the hanging leg-raise which strengthens the lower *rectus abdominis*. Use a chinning bar for this exercise.

What To Do
Jump up and grasp the bar with an overhand grip, hands about shoulder-width apart. Now raise up

(b)

your legs together until they are at waist-height. Hold them in this position, then slowly lower them back to the start position. Try not to swing from front to back to aid the lifting movement. Carry on until the muscles fail. You can raise your legs much higher if you wish, until they touch the bar, either holding them together or wide apart. You will probably find that your arms give out long before your abs., so this exercise is really only beneficial if you are already strong in your upper body.

48. *Incline Sit-Ups*

EXERCISE STRESS: This stresses mainly the upper part of the *rectus abdominis* muscle group.

What To Do
Arrange an abdominal board at a suitable angle of incline for yourself and lie back on it, hooking your feet under the rollers at the top end. Bend your knees and move your bottom as high up the board as you can and keep it there. Put both hands behind your head. Raise up your head and shoulders and slowly curl upwards, rounding your back, until your head can touch your knees. Then very slowly lie back down again in a curling movement. Do not go back all the way down. Keep the tension on your stomach and do not relax it at any point. Keep your head and shoulders up. Repeat.

Variations
In order to stress the oblique muscles as well, you can twist as you sit up, touching your right elbow to your left knee, and your left elbow to your right knee alternately.

When the exercise becomes easier, you can either increase the angle of incline, increase the number of reps or hold a light barbell plate on your chest.

Incline Sit-Ups With Twist (a)

(b)

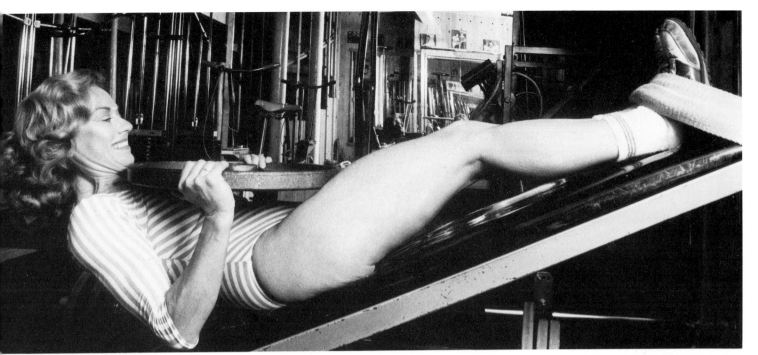

Incline Negative Sit-Ups (a)

(b)

49. *Incline Negative Sit-Ups*

EXERCISE STRESS: The whole front abdominal wall. This is a heavy building exercise, which I have always found particularly effective.

What To Do
Lie back on an inclined abdominal board, as for ordinary sit-ups. Sit up, with bent legs, and get a spotter to hand you a heavy barbell plate. Hold this across your chest with both hands. From an upright position, lie back as slowly as you possibly can, resisting gravity all the way. At the bottom, do not relax. Keep your head up. In this position take the weight off your chest and hold it forwards at arm's length, so that you can sit up without the extra resistance on your chest. Once upright, replace it on your chest and repeat the movement. The benefit lies in the negative action, against the force of gravity. Repeat.

Tip
You should perform only three sets of six to ten reps of this exercise twice each week, like any other bodypart.

50. *Crunches*

EXERCISE STRESS: The *rectus abdominis* muscle group is strengthened by doing crunches.

What To Do
Select a heavy exercise bench or rest a heavy barbell against an exercise bench to hold it down. Lie down on the floor with your legs raised up across the width of the bench, and your feet hanging off the edge. You

can ask a spotter to sit on your feet to hold them down if necessary.

Hold your hands behind your head and raise your head and shoulders off the floor. Slowly curl up as high as you can. Try to sit up so that your chest reaches your knees. Most women will get nowhere near this position to start with. You should feel a really tight contraction in the stomach muscles. Lower yourself back down slowly. Do not collapse flat or relax. Keeping the tension on your stomach, sit up again. Repeat.

Tips
The exercise is easier the further from the bench you place your bottom, so try to keep it tucked in close.

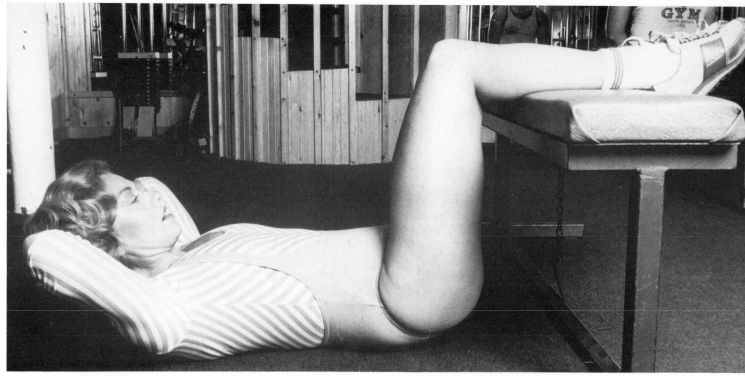

Crunches (a)

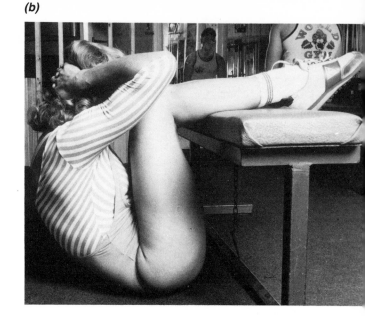

(b)

You should never flap up and down quickly, raising your hips off the floor, thereby adding momentum to the movement. This will completely destroy the whole effect. Keep it slow and limit the range of movement to whatever you can manage, provided that you can really feel it working.

Variations
You can involve the side muscles that pull in the waist by twisting as you sit up. Touch your right elbow to your left knee and vice versa. This is tough, but exceptionally effective. After one work-out you should see a difference. I find that 4×50 reps pull my waist in at least half an inch in one session.

51. *Rope Crunches*

EXERCISE STRESS: The whole of the front abdominal area. This is a good exercise to finish off your abdominal exercise routine.

What To Do
Attach a rope or a short bar handle to the overhead pulley on a machine. Kneel down on the floor facing the machine and pull the rope down in front of your head or behind your neck. Hold it in this position throughout the exercise. Now bend forward until your forehead touches the floor. At the same time, tense the whole stomach and exhale forcefully. Slowly return to the upright position and repeat.

Tips
Use a deliberate, slow movement and concentrate on using your abs. and not your arms throughout.

Chapter Five

BEGINNERS' AND INTERMEDIATE WORK-OUTS

The work-outs described in this section progress through the following stages:

BEGINNERS' LEVEL
(start to 6 months)

Stage 1   Pre-Weight-Training Conditioning (6–8 weeks)
Purpose: for fitness, endurance and flexibility.

Stage 2   Weight-Training Conditioning (6–8 weeks)
Purpose: to learn to handle weights, coordination, skill and balance.
To further develop fitness, local muscle endurance, and overall stamina.

Stage 3   First Level Bodybuilding (6–8 weeks)
1 First application of progressive overload for muscle stimulation.
2 Fitness training.
3 Muscular endurance training.
4 Body-conditioning for improving fast recovery of muscles and all back-up systems.

Stage 4   Second Level Bodybuilding (6–8 weeks)
Increased intensity for further all-round conditioning and muscular endurance.

INTERMEDIATE LEVEL
(6 months onwards)

1 The number of sets and reps is gradually increased to the maximum level the body can tolerate in one work-out.

2 When the muscles and cardio-vascular system are sufficiently adapted, a split routine is introduced.

3 Training becomes much more intense within each set, working to failure each time.

4 Training concentrates on building muscle mass and density.

ADVANCED AND PRE-COMPETITIVE LEVEL
(described in Chapter 6)

1 The number of sets is reduced, but more specialized intensification techniques are used (e.g. negatives, forced reps and supersets). A training partner becomes mandatory at this stage.

2 A personalized programme is introduced to improve individual figure proportions.

3 Pre-planned training and dietary cycles are followed all year round.

4 Pre-competitive split routine schedules are introduced when required.

5 Individual training techniques and intensive training principles are followed.

BEGINNERS' LEVEL WORK-OUTS

Stage 1: Pre-Weight Training Conditioning

This schedule should be performed every other day, for about 6 to 8 weeks. It should be done reasonably fast, with as little rest between sets and reps as possible, though you must take it easily at first. Start with one set of each exercise, with the lowest number of reps indicated, for Week 1. Advance to two sets for Week 2, and three sets for Weeks 3 to 6.

Work up the number of reps to the maximum indicated. If you can do more than the number indicated for the waist exercises, then carry on. For all the other exercises, if you find the number of reps easy, then work faster.

On alternate days, do some form of aerobic exercise (e.g. jogging, swimming, dancing, cycling) for 10 to 20 minutes, working up to 40 minutes. This will aid in your weight loss programme, as well as helping general fitness. Watch your diet!

Stage 2: Weight-Training Conditioning

You will have to use your judgment about the point at which you start to use weights. If you are really unfit, very overweight or over thirty-five, then start with the pre-conditioning exercise programme and don't rush things. If you have been exercising regularly (e.g. in aerobic classes, swimming, etc.), then by all means start at Stage 2. This will enable you to handle light weights from the start.

Handling free weights is not easy and requires a considerable degree of skill which must be learnt. Coordination, balance and correct breathing are initially much more important than strength improvement, so the weight you use will be nominal. The vast majority of beginners are very nervous about handling weights. The limitation is invariably ninety percent mental. Women have been conditioned to expect to be weak, so the idea of pressing a barbell overhead really unnerves them. At first you will probably feel very wobbly, ungainly, and uncoordinated. Don't worry about

Bodypart	Exercise	Sets	Reps
STAGE 1: PRE-WEIGHT TRAINING CONDITIONING (Purpose: Fitness, endurance, flexibility)			
Waist	1. Sit-Ups (or Half-Jack-knives)	1–3	10–15
	2. Leg-Raise	1–3	10–15
	3. Twists	2	50
Legs	4. Free Squats	1–3	15–20
	5. Side Leg-Raise	1–3	15–20
	6. Back Leg-Raise	1–3	15–20
	7. Inner Thigh-Raise	3	25
Chest	8. Flyes	1–3	10–12
Shoulders	9. Shrugs	1–3	10–12
	10. Lateral Raises	1–3	10–12
Back	11. Good Mornings	1–3	10–12
Arms	12. Biceps Curl	1–3	10–12
	13. Triceps Dip	1–3	10–12
Calves	14. Calf-Raises	3	15

Bodypart	Exercise	Sets	Reps
STAGE 2: WEIGHT-TRAINING CONDITIONING (Purpose: General Conditioning) 5-minute warm-up			
Waist	1. Sit-Ups	1–3	10–25
	2. Leg-Raise	1–3	15–20
	3. Twists	2	100
Legs	4. Squat	1–3	15–20
	5. Leg Curls	1–3	15–20
Chest	6. Bench Press	1–3	10–15
Upper Back	7. Barbell Bentover Row	1–3	10–15
Shoulders	8. Military Press	1–3	10–15
Biceps	9. Barbell Curl	1–3	10–15
Triceps	10. Lying Triceps Extension	1–3	10–15
Calves	11. Calf-Raises	3	15

this! Everybody has to start somewhere, and even 'Miss Olympia' must once have been through this stage. After only a few sessions, the majority of women cope with confidence and look around for extra weight to use.

Follow this programme three times each week (Mon/Wed/Fri or Tues/Thurs/Sat) with a day off in between. Work quickly. On non-weight-training days jog, swim, cycle, etc. for 10 to 40 minutes. Carry on for 6 to 8 weeks with this schedule, depending on your personal condition.

Use minimal weights. The exact amount will depend on the individual, but do not sacrifice strict form.

Start with one set of each exercise and the lowest number of reps recommended, and work up to three sets and the maximum number of reps recommended. Observe all the safety principles outlined in Chapter 3.

Stage 3: First Level Bodybuilding

If you started the pre-weight-training conditioning programme at home, then now is the time to seek out a suitable gym.

This is a proper bodybuilding programme, so use as much weight as you can for each exercise, whilst maintaining 'strict form' (see p. 24).

Perform this routine three times each week with a day's rest in between. The whole work-out should take between 1 and 1½ hours. Work fairly slowly. Rest about 1 to 1½ minutes between sets, longer if you have to.

You can carry on from Week 12 for as long as you wish on this programme. If you are a normal weight for your bodytype (or mesomorphic), limit the amount of aerobic exercise that you do and get plenty of rest between work-outs.

Follow the off-season building diet described in Chapter 8.

If you are underweight for your bodytype (or ectomorphic), follow the weight-gain diet and rest as much as you can. Do not do any form of aerobic exercise.

If you are overweight for your bodytype (or endomorphic), carry on with your aerobic exercise

FIRST LEVEL BODYBUILDING SCHEDULE

(Purpose: Beginners' Bodybuilding Level 1)
5-minute warm-up, spot-jogging, keep-fit exercises or stretches

Bodypart	Exercise	Sets	Reps
Abs.	1. Crunches 2. Off-Bench Leg-Raise 3. Twists	3 3 3	25 25 100
Legs	4. Squats 5. Leg Extensions 6. Leg Curl	4 4 4	15 15 15
Chest	7. Incline Bench Press 8. Flat Flyes	3 3	8–10 8–10
Upper Back	9. Bentover Row	3	8–10
Lower Back	10. Stiff Legged Deadlift* (*Once a week only)	3	8–10
Shoulders	11. Behind Neck Press 12. Lat. Pulldown	3 3	8–10 8–10
Biceps	13. Barbell Curl	3	8–10
Triceps	14. Triceps Extension/or Pulley Pushdown	3	8–10
Wrists	15. Barbell Wrist Curls	3	10–15
Calves	16. Calf-Raises	4	15

every other day, and work as fast as you can with minimal rest periods.

If you have access to either multigym or Nautilus equipment, you can substitute a machine exercise for any of these listed, to add variety. However, keep a good mix of free weights and machines and do not rely on machines alone.

By following this schedule and watching your diet carefully, you should soon notice results.

Stage 4: Second Level Bodybuilding

This work-out is intended more for overall conditioning than mass-building, so train as fast as you can and rest as little as possible between sets.

Use moderate weights and go for ten reps wherever indicated. Try to complete three sets of ten without assistance.

The entire work-out should take between 1 to 1½ hours maximum.

Avoid using machines which will slow you down and stick to free weights.

Follow this schedule for at least 6 to 8 weeks before progressing to the intermediate level work-out. Stage 4 is the last programme in which you will train your whole body in one session, three times a week.

SECOND LEVEL BODYBUILDING SCHEDULE (Purpose: Beginners' Bodybuilding Level 2) 5-minute warm-up			
Bodypart	Exercise	Sets	Reps
Abs.	1. Incline Sit-Ups	2	30
	2. Leg-Raise	2	30
	3. Twists	2	100
Legs	4. Squats	3	12–15
	5. Leg Extensions	3	12–15
	6. Leg Curls	3	12–15
Chest	7. Incline Bench Press	3	8–10
	8. Flat Flyes	3	8–10
Lower Back	9. Stiff Legged Deadlift	2	8–10
Lats.	10. Barbell Bentover Rows	3	8–10
Traps	11. Shrugs	3	8–10
	12. Military Press	3	8–10
Delts.	13. Front Raises	2	8–10
	14. Side Lateral Raises	2	8–10
Biceps	15. Barbell Curls	3	8–10
Triceps	16. Lying Triceps Extensions	3	8–10
Wrists	17. Wrist Curls	2	15
Calves	18. Calf-Raises	6	15

INTERMEDIATE LEVEL WORK-OUTS

This phase should be reached after about six months training depending on the results you are obtaining and can be continued until you decide you are ready to compete. If you are not interested in competing, you can carry on indefinitely with this level of training.

During the preceding six months, you should have experienced some radical improvements in your overall fitness, energy level and appearance. Your bodyfat level should be going down and your metabolic rate up. The beginners' work-outs will have conditioned your body sufficiently to cope with a gradually increasing workload, teaching it to adapt to physical stress and to recover quickly from it. From the first work-out, the total number of exercises, sets and poundages have been stepped up to add intensity and the work-outs have become gradually longer and more taxing. We have now reached the uppermost limit for this system and future work-outs will need to be intensified in a different manner. The reason for this is that a schedule which includes two or three exercises, and eight to ten total sets per bodypart, will be so long that you would not have sufficient energy or stamina to train the entire body in one session.

You may have built up your stamina and energy levels, but there is a limit to the amount the body can take. So although a whole body work-out was possible at beginner's level, at the intermediate level of training it is time to introduce a basic split routine. The top priority at this level is to build up basic muscle bulk particularly on the upper body, where most women are weakest. The way in which this is done is to concentrate on relatively few basic exercises which involve whole groups of muscles, and to use sufficient weight to overload the muscles at all times.

The Four-Day Split System

The four-day split is the basic bodybuilding work-out system and is the one you should follow most of the time. It can be used indefinitely, whether or not you wish to compete, on a year-round basis to maintain excellent condition and shape. Most women will make rapid gains in muscularity and enhance their body shape on this schedule in combination with proper nutrition.

There are three advantages to the four-day split:

1 It allows you to train each bodypart more intensively. You can either train intensively, or you can train for long periods, but it is difficult to do both. Each work-out should last a maximum 1½ hours.

2 You can train each major muscle group twice each week.

3 The split system allows the body a suitable rest period to recover fully, strengthen, grow and prepare for the next work-out. Rest is vital for growth after an intense session. If you are still tired from the previous work-out, the next one will be wasted.

Remember:

Train intensively. Rest thoroughly. Eat properly.

How the Four-Day Split Works

The body is divided into two sections, and each section is trained twice each week.

Mon	Tues	Wed	Thurs	Fri	Sat	Sun
A	B	Rest	A	B	Rest	Rest

Dividing up the body can be done in one of two ways:

1 The first method involves training the trunk one day, the limbs the next:

Mon/Thurs	Tues/Fri
Abs.	Abs.
Chest	Legs
Shoulders	Biceps
Back	Calves
Calves	

2 The second system divides up the muscles which push and pull as follows:

Mon/Thurs	Tues/Fri
Abs.	Abs.
Chest	Legs
Shoulders	Back
Triceps	Biceps
Calves	Calves

If you have a very weak bodypart, you can train it separately on Wednesdays. Abs. and calves should be trained daily. I tend to train my legs when I know I do not have to work-out next day. Leg sessions are always tough and I feel the need for extra recovery time.

Here is a suggested four-day split routine using the 'push-pull' division of muscle groups. If you have access to Nautilus, Polaris, or multigym machines, you can substitute exercises as you wish. You should read the notes on Off-Season Training Cycle principles before you start (p. 138).

STAGE 2: FOUR-DAY SPLIT INTERMEDIATE BODYBUILDING SCHEDULE
(System 1)
Mon/Thurs   5-minute warm-up or stretching

Bodypart	Exercise	Type	Sets	Total Sets Per Bodypart	Reps
Abs.	Sit-Ups	Basic	4		20
	Crunches	Isolation	4	10	20
	Twists	Isolation	2		100
Chest	Incline Bench Press	Basic	3		6–8
	Flat Flyes	Isolation	3	9	6–8
	Pullovers	Isolation	3		6–8
Shoulders	Upright Row	Basic	3		6–8
	Press Behind Neck	Basic	3	9	6–8
	Side Lateral Raise	Isolation	3		6–8
Delts	Side Lateral Raise	Isolation	3	3	6–8
Triceps	Lying Triceps Extensions	Basic	3	6	6–8
	Pulley Pushdowns	Isolation	3		6–8
Forearms	Reverse Curl	Basic	3	3	6–8
Calves	Calf-Raises	Basic	6	6	15

Tues/Fri 5-minute warm-up or stretching						
Abs.	Off-Bench Leg-Raise Incline Sit-Ups with a Twist	Basic Basic	4 4 2	10	25 25 100
Legs	Squats Leg Extensions Leg Curls	Basic Isolation Isolation	4 4 4	12	10–12 10–12 10–12
Lower Back	Stiff Legged Deadlift* (*once a week only)	Basic	3		6–8
Upper Back	Barbell Bentover Rowing Lat. Machine Pulldowns	Basic Isolation	3 3	6	6–8 6–8
Biceps	Barbell Curls	Basic	3		6–8
Calves	Calf-Raises	Basic	6		15

Here is the same basic work-out, but rearranged into the trunk/limbs division of bodyparts or 'Upper body/Lower body' system. Again, these exercises are merely suggestions. You can reorganize the schedule to suit your own personal physique problem.

STAGE 2: FOUR-DAY SPLIT INTERMEDIATE BODYBUILDING SCHEDULE
(System 2)

Mon/Thurs   5-minute warm-up

Bodypart	Exercise	Sets	Reps
Abs.	Jack-Knife Twists Crunches Twists	4 4 2	20 20 100
Chest	Incline Bench Press Flat Flyes Pullover	3 3 3	6–8 6–8 6–8
Upper Back	Barbell Bentover Rowing Lat. Machine Pulldowns	3 3	6–8 6–8
Lower Back	Stiff Legged Deadlift* (*once a week only)	3	6–8
Calves	Calf-Raises	6	15

Tues/Fri   5-minute warm-up or stretching

Bodypart	Exercise	Sets	Reps
Abs.	Off-Bench Leg-Raises Incline Sit-Ups Twists	4 4 2	25 25 100
Chest	Squats Leg Extensions Leg Curls	4 4 4	10–12 10–12 10–12
Biceps	Barbell Curls	3	6–8
Calves	Calf-Raises	6	15

The Eight- And Twelve-Day Cycle

This is an alternative intermediate level split system which I have found particularly beneficial at the start of off-season training for regaining both strength and mass after the competitive season. It gives plenty of time for recovery and is a good system to follow if you have a busy life.

This system divides the body into two (or even three) sections and works them on alternate days, which means that working each bodypart twice will take you eight days and three times, twelve. Use the bodypart divisions as for the four-day split.

EIGHT-DAY CYCLE

	Mon	Tues	Wed	Thurs	Fri	Sat	Sun
Week 1	A	Rest	B	Rest	A	Rest	B
Week 2	Mon Rest	**New Cycle** Tues A	Wed Rest	Thurs B	Fri Rest	Sat A	Sun Rest

TWELVE-DAY CYCLE

	Mon	Tues	Wed	Thurs	Fri	Sat	Sun
Week 1	A	Rest	B	Rest	C	Rest	A
Week 2	Mon Rest	Tues B	Wed Rest	Thurs C	Fri Rest	**New Cycle** Sat A	Sun Rest

Use the bodyparts divisions as for the 4-day split.

CONSTRUCTING A SCHEDULE

It is of vital importance for your continuing bodybuilding progress to understand how to construct your own programmes. The principal reason is that at present there are very few gyms where women's bodybuilding is either taught or understood. If you rely on having your programme devised for you by an inexpert or unsympathetic instructor, you will lose time, energy, money and enthusiasm.

It is far better to know exactly what you want and how to achieve it yourself. By the application of an intelligent and systematic approach you can be your own trainer and vary your work-outs according to your progress. This is where the magic of bodybuilding really begins, because you can literally sculpt your own body into a new shape like an artist.

The needs of each individual are going to be different, so at this stage it is not possible to recommend one work-out schedule for everyone which will turn them into 'Miss Olympia'. Instead, you need to understand the principles of body sculpture and how you as an individual can apply these principles to devise the programme which will work best for yourself. You should therefore decide:

1 Exactly what you want to achieve.
2 What level of training you are at.
3 What specific faults there are in your figure.

Basic Principles

The same exercises are used to achieve weight-loss or weight-gain, conditioning, etc., but they can be put together to achieve any result you may choose. It is the way in which schedules are constructed which is important because different effects are achieved by changing the number of reps and sets and the amount of weight used. However, certain fundamental rules apply:

To Achieve:	Apply:
1 Strength and Muscular weight-gain	heavy weight and low reps (4–6).
2 Muscular endurance	light weight and high reps (15–20).
3 Cardio-vascular fitness (slimming and definition)	light weight and fast, high reps (15–20).
4 Power	large muscle group exercises which involve dynamic force. Use very low reps or the pyramid system (see p. 104). (1–2–3–4–5).
5 Detailed muscle shape	medium reps (8–10) and moderate weight with short rest intervals.

How to Construct Your Personal Exercise Schedule

Decide on the level of training you require, and refer to the specimen schedules in this chapter. You will need to modify them to suit your individual physique problems.

Decide which exercise system you propose to use (e.g. Beginners' three-day per week schedule, intermediate four-day split, etc.) and which system of bodypart division you prefer, if you select a split system.

On a clean sheet of paper lay out the following format:

Date	HEADING (Type of Schedule) (e.g. INTERMEDIATE LEVEL 2) Purpose (e.g. Conditioning, bodybuilding, etc)			
Bodypart	*Exercise*	*Type*	*Sets*	*Reps*

Next, fill in the left-hand column (bodyparts to be trained), bearing in mind the following principles:

■ **Abdominal exercises** are often done first because

  a. They are a very good form of warm-up. They get the blood circulating into the muscles and put you in the mood.

  b. They do not (at the beginners' stage anyway) require weights, so you will not be in danger of straining cold muscles.

  c. Tummy exercises are not the most popular. If you leave them until the end of your work-out, you will probably skip them altogether. If they are at the beginning, they are unavoidable.

  d. The weakest bodyparts should be trained first while you are freshest. For most women, abdominals certainly fit the bill! There are people who prefer doing abdominals at the end. It is safer to do so at the end of a leg work-out.

■ **Major muscle groups** are always trained next, using exercises which involve whole groups of muscles, such as the squat, bench press, bentover rows, etc. This means leg, back, chest, shoulders in that order.

These exercises use a lot of energy. They are used mainly for building muscle bulk and density.

■ **Small muscles** are trained last (e.g. biceps, triceps, forearms and calves). If you trained any of these muscles at the start of your programme, they would be too tired to lift the heavier weights of the major muscle group exercises later on.

■ The only occasion when you should ignore this order of exercising is if you have a lagging bodypart which you wish to hit really hard. In that instance, you should exercise it right at the start of your work-out, regardless of the usual order. This is called **muscle priority training**. If your weak area happens to be your arms, then train them on a separate night or you will not be able to do the rest of your work-out at all. The same applies to your calves on a leg night.

■ **Groups of muscles** which work in direct opposition as in pushing and pulling (e.g. biceps and triceps, leg biceps and quadriceps) are usually worked alternately.

Choose the exercise you intend to use for each bodypart. Select one *basic* exercise, plus one or two *isolation* exercises from the list given on p. 42. For instance, for the *biceps* you could use barbell curl (basic) and preacher curl (isolation); for the *upper back*, use bentover row (basic) and lat. machine pulldowns (isolation); for the *shoulders*, use upright rows (basic) and shrugs (isolation).

Bear in mind your specific weaknesses when making your choice. Select basic exercises for areas which need building up; go for more isolation exercises in areas where you are fairly muscular or need to reduce fat levels.

Fill in your exercise schedule with the selected exercise and its type (basic or isolation). This will teach you to recognize which exercises are which.

Next, decide on the number of sets and reps you should use. These are the rules to follow for the average intermediate bodybuilding schedule:

To Build Muscle

a. *Upper Body*

Use 8 to 10 total sets per bodypart with low reps (6 to 10 maximum). Perform exercises slowly and rest between sets. Use as much weight as possible. For example:

For the Bust	Sets		Reps
Bench Press	3	×	6–10
Flat Flyes	3	×	6–10
Incline Flyes	3	×	6–10
For the Triceps			
Triceps Extensions	3	×	6–10
Pulley Pushdown	3	×	6–10
Dips	2–3	×	Maximum

b. *Lower Body*

The number of reps performed for lower body muscles is usually higher because the muscles are bigger and stronger. Use 10 to 12 reps per muscle group, 3 to 4 sets of each. For example:

For the Legs	Sets		Reps
Squats	3–4	×	10–12
Leg Extensions	3	×	10–12
Leg Bicep Curls	3	×	10–12

Intensify your training by adding extra sets. More advanced trainers can increase the total number to 12, employing 3 sets of 4 different exercises for the same bodypart.

The calves are small muscles but they are in constant use, carrying your bodyweight around. As a result, you should use *very* heavy weights (start with 150–200 lbs at least) – and employ high sets and reps. I suggest 6 times 15. Train them at the end of every work-out, except on leg training days.

To Reduce Weight

Use 3 sets per exercise, 15–20 reps each set. Rest as little as possible between sets. Perform exercises fast with moderate weights.

This type of schedule will not 'spot' reduce but will tone up the muscle groups you work, in combination with the right diet.

Recording Your Work-Out

On the right-hand side of your exercise schedule leave an empty column for notes.

When you have devised your latest training schedule, either transcribe it into your training diary or obtain a number of Xerox copies. Take these with you to the gym. When you work-out, make detailed notes in the right-hand column as you go along of the number of reps and sets you actually managed to perform and the amount of weight you used. For example, if you managed one set of eight reps using 20 lbs of weight for a biceps exercise you could write: $1 \times 8 \times 20$. Keep all your old notes to chart your progress and see what works for you. You should employ the following bodybuilding shorthand. For example:

Exercise	Sets	Reps	Actual Performance		
			Sets per set	Reps	Weight used in lbs or kilos
Biceps	3	6–8	1 ×	8 ×	20
			1 ×	8 ×	20
			1 ×	6 ×	25

Your completed personal exercise schedule, using a four-day split at the intermediate level, could therefore look like this:

Date	**INTERMEDIATE LEVEL 2 (Four-Day Split – Part 1)** *Purpose – Bodybuilding (Building Phase)* *Muscle Division System 'Push/Pull'* **Mon/Thurs**					
Bodypart	*Exercise*	*Type*	*Sets*	*Reps*	*Notes*
Abs.	Sit-Ups Leg-Raise Twists	Basic Basic Isolation	3 3 2	20 20 50–100	
Chest	Bench Press Flat Flyes Pullovers	Basic Isolation Isolation	3 3 3	6–8 6–8 6–8	
Shoulders	Upright Row Press Behind Neck	Basic Basic	3 3	6–8 6–8	
Delts.	Front Raise Side Lateral Raise Bentover Lateral Raise	Isolation Isolation Isolation	3 3 3	6–8 6–8 6–8	
Triceps	Lying Triceps Extension Pulley Pushdowns	Basic Isolation	3 3	6–8 6–8	
Forearms	Reverse Curl	Basic	3	6–8	
Calves	Calf-Raises	Basic	6	15	

CHANGING THE PEAR-SHAPED WOMAN INTO A BODYBUILDER

Let us now consider the pear-shaped woman as a 'case history' of what a bodybuilding programme can achieve in terms of figure reproportioning.

The Problems
1 Weak, undeveloped upper body.
2 Not much waistline.
3 Small bust.
4 Big bottom, thighs, hips or stomach.

The Overall Aim
To reshape the contours of the body.

Requirements
1 Broaden the shoulders to give the illusion of a narrower waist.
2 Build up the arms.
3 Improve the bustline.
4 Reduce the waistline.
5 Reduce lower-body fat deposits.

The Method

1 Exercises to broaden the shoulders (which include those for the trapezius, deltoids and *latissimus dorsi*). All of these will enhance the triangular effect. The best exercises to choose from are as follows:

Shoulders	Upright rowing, military press, behind neck press, incline shoulder press.
Lats.	Bentover rowing, lat. pulldowns, seated rowing, chins.
Delts.	Front lateral raise, side lateral raise, bentover lateral raise.

2 Exercises to build up the arms:

Biceps	Barbell curls, incline dumb-bell curls.
Triceps	Lying triceps extensions, pulley pushdown, dips.
Forearms	Reverse curls.
Wrists	Wrist curls, reverse wrist curls.

3 Improving the bustline. I've yet to meet any woman who was satisfied with this aspect of her anatomy. Everyone seems to think they are too small, too big, too saggy or some other real or imagined fault. As you lose bodyfat, you will inevitably lose size off your bust because it is composed primarily of fatty tissue. Unless you choose to resort to plastic surgery, the only way of increasing your bust size is to build up the underlying pectoral muscles which help to support the breasts, thereby improving your shape. Building your 'pecs' will also give you a terrific cleavage.

Choose a combination of chest exercises from the following: bench press, incline bench press, pec. deck flyes, flat flyes, incline flyes or cable cross-overs.

4 Reducing the waistline and flattening the stomach. Work your abs. every day until you begin to see an improvement, then continue every other day. You can do these at the start of your main work-out as a warm-up, but if you find it too exhausting, work your abs. separately in the morning or during your lunchbreak.

Remember, no amount of ab. work will be effective unless you watch your diet too.

Use any combination of abdominal exercise, such as sit-ups, leg-raises, crunches, jack-knives, sit-ups with a twist, hanging leg-raises.

5 Reducing lower body fat deposits. There are two ways of approaching this problem, and you will have to decide which appeals to you. The first is a fast, intensive aerobic work-out. Select exercises such as lunges, free squats, leg curls, leg extensions, back leg raises, donkey kicks, all performed in sequence, using 15 to 20 reps each, with short rest intervals.

This is a good method to use if you are very overweight, or preparing for a contest. However, if you are patient then slow heavy weight-training combined with sensible diet will eventually have the same effect and is a much more enjoyable method. Select heavy leg exercises from squats, leg extensions, leg curls, leg press and hack squats.

From this example, you will see that once you have analysed where your problems lie, you can then invent your own work-out schedule to correct them.

As you train consistently, your figure faults will vary as your proportions change. When you notice this happening, it is time to take a critical look at your physique and alter your training programme to accommodate the developments. Some areas of your body will respond to training fast, others will lag behind. Always work the weak areas hardest and concentrate on developing them to the level of your best areas. If you have some good features, you can afford to train them less frequently, in the knowledge that they will catch up rapidly. If you always work on good areas, you will quickly develop an unbalanced physique. You can see examples of this in any gym. Many young men, for instance, train to develop showy arms and hardly develop their legs at all, with bizarre results.

If you have any bodypart with overdeveloped muscularity, then stop training that area with heavy weights altogether. Work it as little as possible – just enough to maintain muscle tone, and no more. Keep reps high and weights low.

Chapter Six

ADVANCED TRAINING METHODS AND WORK-OUTS

Quality training is based on the concept of reducing the amount of time taken to perform the same work-out. This is done by drastically reducing rest intervals between sets, and also by introducing sophisticated high-intensity techniques.

Quality training can be employed for short periods at any time in your regular work-outs at the intermediate and advanced levels. It is particularly useful for breaking through 'plateau' periods, when development appears to be at a halt. Be careful not to overdo it, or you may end up overtraining.

Quality training is primarily useful as a pre-competitive technique because with disciplined dieting it produces the best possible combination of muscle mass, density and definition.

General intensity can be increased at any time in the following ways:

1 Reducing the amount of time to perform the same work-out.
2 Reducing rest intervals between sets and reps.
3 Keeping to the same weight, but increasing the number of sets and reps.
4 Lifting more weight, or adding more resistance.
5 Doing more work-outs in the week.

SPECIFIC INTENSIFICATION TECHNIQUES USED IN QUALITY TRAINING

Remember, with all high-intensity techniques to start with caution or you will risk overtraining and injury. Your muscles and system must be adapted slowly to cope. Begin with one all-out work-out in each week and build up slowly to two or three each week. Alternate intensity training with weeks of lower intensity. Always work a set to normal failure using strict form, before adding an intensity technique.

1. *Training to Failure*

This involves working a set until your muscles cannot possibly complete another rep. You should continue trying to lift (with the help of your training partner), until you can only do half a rep or a quarter rep, and eventually cannot lift at all, and just stall. To stop short of muscle failure will never build muscle. You will encounter a real mental barrier, as well as a physical one, using this technique. It is going to hurt you and you must force yourself to push right through the 'pain zone', yet still go on. If you are training to failure, *never* work alone; always use a spotter, or even two, especially when performing the bench press or squats.

2. *Supersets*

Supersets consist of two exercises performed in rapid succession with no rest between them. They can be applied in two ways:
a. Exercises using opposing or 'antagonistic' muscles.
b. Exercising muscles in the same group.

Of these types of supersets, the second form is more intensive than the first, concentrating as it does on exhausting one bodypart only. Do not rest within supersets. Allow 30 to 40 seconds only between them and continue to use as much weight as possible.

Here are some examples of superset combinations employing antagonistic muscles:

Bodypart	Muscles Involved	Superset Exercises
1 Legs	Quadriceps and leg biceps	Leg extensions and leg curls
2 Chest and back	Pectorals and lats.	Bench press and pulldowns
3 Arms	Biceps and triceps	Barbell curls and triceps extensions

Here are some examples of supersets for one muscle group only:

Bodypart	Muscles Involved	Superset Exercises
1 Legs	Quadriceps	Squats and leg extensions
2 Chest	Pectorals	Bench press and flyes
3 Back	Lats.	Chins and seated pulley rowing
4 Arms	Biceps	Barbell curls and concentration curls
	Triceps	Triceps extension and dumb-bell behind neck press

In a quality training work-out schedule, supersets would be grouped together throughout. Here is part of a possible pre-contest schedule using supersets:

Superset Exercise	Type of Superset
Squat Leg Press	2
Leg Extension Leg Curl	1
Bentover Row Lat. Pulldown	2
Pull-overs Shrugs	1
Incline Curl Concentration Curl	2
Wrist Curl Reverse Wrist Curl	2
Seated Calf-Raises Standing Calf-Raises	2

3. Trisets

Trisets consist of three exercises performed without rest intervals one after the other, usually for a single complex bodypart, such as the thighs, back or chest.

Here are some examples of trisets:

Bodypart	Muscles	Triset
1 Thighs	Quadriceps	Squat, leg press and leg extension
2 Back	Lats, traps erector spinae	Pulldowns and shrugs and hyperextensions
3 Chest	Pectorals	Incline bench press, flat flyes and cross-bench pull-overs

4. *Giant Sets*

In order to achieve a championship level of shapeliness and finish for the physique, some advanced bodybuilders employ a technique known as 'giant sets'. It is not actually possible to shape sections of an individual muscle. Rather, each muscle group has to be moulded and refined to gain a fully developed contour. Giant sets are the most sophisticated method of achieving this end.

Four or more exercises are used in rapid sequence for a specific bodypart, using only 1 or 2 sets each. This isolates each muscle within the group, working it as intensively as possible. There should be little or no rest between exercises.

Here is an example of a giant set for the biceps:

Purpose	Exercise	Type
Mass/Strength	Barbell curl	Basic
Peak	Concentration curl	Isolation
Inner Biceps/Mass	Incline curl	Isolation
Brachialis/Mass	Reverse curls	Isolation

A giant set for the chest might comprise the following:

Purpose	Exercise	Type
Mass/Strength	Bench press	Basic
Inner Pec. Definition	Pec. dec.	Isolation
Upper Pec. Mass	Incline press	Basic
General Pec. Definition	Flat flyes	Isolation

5. *Pre-Exhaustion*

When you perform an exercise which involves large groups of muscles, (e.g. squat, bench press), the smaller muscles form a weak link and fail first. This means that you cannot sufficiently stress the larger ones, which you actually want to reach, to induce growth. In order to counteract this situation, pre-exhaustion can be used to partly fatigue the stronger muscles, so that the weaker ones do not give out before they are fully stressed.

The technique involves supersetting an isolation movement for a major bodypart, with a heavy basic exercise for the same muscles. Here are some examples:

Bodypart	Muscles	Exercises
1 Chest	Pectorals	Flyes and bench press
2 Legs	Quadriceps	Leg extensions and squats
3 Back	Lats.	Dumb-bell rowing and barbell bent-over rows
4 Shoulders	Delts.	Lateral raises and military press

To employ pre-exhaustion training involves a little preliminary organization. The pre-exhausted muscle will recover fast, so you must set up your equipment for the second exercise in advance to capitalize on the training situation you create.

GOING BEYOND MUSCLE FAILURE

The ultimate in training intensity for developing high-density muscle mass involves going beyond muscle failure. There are several techniques you can employ to do this. Training past failure is the mark of a real bodybuilder. This type of high-intensity training is painful because fatigue toxins build up rapidly in a muscle worked past failure. This deep 'burn' is actively sought by advanced trainers who know it signifies gains in strength, mass and general progress. This is the basis of the old bodybuilding adage, 'No pain, no gain'. Unfortunately, it happens to be true!

1. *Cheating*

I have already mentioned cheating (on p. 24) as an incorrect form of training to be avoided by beginners, but it can also be used as an advanced technique to make an exercise much harder and to work a muscle beyond failure. The difference is that beginners cheat to remove stress from a muscle group. Advanced trainers cheat to place greater stress on a working muscle. The main point to remember is that you should perform a normal set in strict form first and then cheat just enough to get the bar up to perform two or three final reps. The most common exercise for which cheating is employed is the barbell curl.

First of all, load the bar with as much weight as you can handle and perform 6 to 8 reps in strict form. When you reach the point of failure and cannot raise the bar beyond the sticking point, swing your body sufficiently to involve the muscles of the back, which will enable you to complete the lift. Hold the bar at the top of the movement, then lower it as slowly as possible, on your own, resisting gravity all the way. This is vital, since you will get the maximum benefit from this movement. Repeat for 2 to 3 cheating reps only. This technique is convenient because it can be done alone and does not require a training partner, unless you are using it for bench presses.

2. *Forced Reps*

This technique allows you to perform 2 or 3 extra reps beyond the point where you could do them alone. You will require a training partner to aid you in breaking through the failure barrier. First of all, work the set to personal failure. Let us suppose it is a seated press behind neck and your training partner stands ready behind you. When you can no longer lift beyond your sticking point, your partner supports the bar just enough to reduce the actual weight by a few pounds, thus enabling you to complete the lift. You then lower the bar alone, resisting its downward movement all the way. Your partner can add resistance to the bar as you lower it, forcing you to work even more intensely. For the succeeding reps your partner aids you increasingly, until your muscles totally fail.

3. *Partial Reps*

You can try this technique with a partner. Let us take the barbell curl as an example. Use a heavier weight than you would normally be able to lift for this exercise. Instead of raising the bar from knees to shoulders in one movement (i.e. from full extension to full flexion), raise it halfway only, then lower slowly. Perform 3 sets to failure, plus a couple of forced reps. After you have completed 3 sets, perform the second half of the curl immediately as follows: Your partner helps you to raise the bar to your shoulders, lower it yourself, slowly, to the halfway (waist level) position, then raise it again. Perform 3 sets to failure plus forced reps.

This technique will produce a real 'pump' and burn in the biceps, and induce a massive stimulus to growth.

4. *Negatives*

Once you reach positive failure in a set, you can still perform 'negatives', using the downward phase of a movement. This technique requires one or even two training partners. Choose a weight which you could not possibly lift on your own. Get your partners to lift it into position and then lower it on your own, resisting all the way unless your muscles fail. This slow movement against gravity is critical for maximum benefit. Make certain your spotters are standing ready and alert. This technique can induce sudden muscular failure – not to mention lack of nerve!

5. *Descending Sets*

With this technique, load on to a barbell a number of light plates (2½ to 5 kilos). With a spotter at each end of the bar, perform your set to failure. At this point your partners should strip off a plate at each end and you should immediately perform a further set to failure, using the lighter weight. Then your partners should strip off two more plates and you repeat the exercise for a third set. The number of reps you perform will obviously need to increase. Two or three sets done in this manner will usually be sufficient to exhaust the muscles completely.

SOME OTHER USEFUL TECHNIQUES

1. *Peak Contraction*

The object of peak contraction is to apply maximum resistance to the muscle at the point when it is fully contracted. To stimulate maximum growth optimum stress should be maintained for 3 or 4 seconds. Exercises which achieve this objective include concentration curls, leg extensions, leg curls, dumb-bell kickbacks, pec. dec. flyes, shrugs and upright rows.

2. *Slow, Continuous Tension*

This is an excellent pre-contest technique for bringing out maximum striations in your muscles, and for developing muscles at their limits.

The principle is to move the weight very slowly through the full range of movement of an exercise from start to finish. At no time should momentum be involved, which would rob the exercise of its effect. You should really *feel* the weight stressing each area of the muscle.

3. *Iso-Tension Contraction*

This technique is excellent for hardening-off muscles before a contest. It does not involve the use of weights at all, and merely consists of flexing your various muscles very hard, and holding the contraction for about 10 seconds. If you repeat this regularly, you will soon notice results. Competitive bodybuilders automatically apply iso-tension in their pre-contest posing practice, but it can also be practised in the gym between sets. All that posing in front of the mirror isn't just for vanity!

You can work your calves while waiting for the bus by rising on your toes and flexing hard.

POWER TRAINING AND THE PYRAMID SYSTEM

Maximum power (and strength) does not depend on muscle bulk, but on the strength of the connective tissue of ligaments, tendons and cartilages as well as the ability of your body to mobilize the greatest number of muscle fibres fast.

Here are some circumstances in which power training would be beneficial:

1 For basic off-season foundation work.
2 To increase general strength, in order to handle more weight in your bodybuilding work-outs.
3 To recover your strength, after definition training and dieting for a contest.
4 For specific sport training, as in heavy field athletics and power-lifting.

This system enables you to approach near maximum weights for every exercise, at each training session. It concentrates on using the basic exercises with very heavy weights and low reps to stimulate the major muscle groups. You cannot employ many exercises in a schedule for power training because the intensity you use would quickly cause overtraining.

'Pyramiding' works extremely quickly and effectively to build strength and mass and is ideal for off-season bodybuilding training. However, it will not generally benefit you in a pre-competitive phase.

The pyramid system works as follows:

■ Four, five or six sets of an exercise are performed.

■ Each set consists of a decreasing number of reps (e.g. 12, 10, 8, 6).

■ The amount of weight used increases as the reps decrease (e.g. 60, 80, 90, 100 lbs).

■ The first two sets, using high reps and low weight, act as a warm-up for the muscle, in preparation for the heavy work to come.

■ Subsequent sets stress the muscle more intensively each time, until the final set of 4 or 2 reps is performed with virtually maximum weight.

■ After you complete the final maximum intensity set, perform a fast set of 15–20 reps with a light weight. This will make the muscles really pump with blood and 'burn'.

Here is an example of how to pyramid a set of bench presses, assuming you are doing 5 sets. The weights listed are only an example, not a guideline. Use the amount suited to your own strength level.

Sets	Reps	Weight (lbs)
1	10	80
2	8	85
3	6	90
4	4	95
5	2	100
'Pump' Set		
1	15–20	20–25

Here is a suggested Four-Day Split routine for power training.

FOUR-DAY SPLIT POWER TRAINING SCHEDULE (PART 1)
Mon/Thurs

Warm-Up: Powercleans		3	10–12
Exercise	Type	Sets	Reps
Sit-ups with a weight	Basic	3	10–15
Squats	Basic	5	10:8:6:4:2
Barbell bent rows	Basic	4	8:6:4:2
Dumb-bell shrugs	Isolation	4	10:8:6:4
Deadlifts	Basic	3	8:6:4
Barbell curls	Basic	4	8:6:4:2
Reverse wrist curls	Isolation	4	8:6:4:2
Calf-raises	Basic	6	15

FOUR-DAY SPLIT POWER TRAINING SCHEDULE (PART 2)

Tues/Fri

Warm-Up: Powercleans		3	10–12
Exercise	Type	Sets	Reps
Off-bench leg-raise with weights	Basic	3	10–15
Incline bench press	Basic	5	10:8:6:4:2
Military press	Basic	4	8:6:4:2
Barbell pull-overs	Isolation	4	8:6:4:2
Lying triceps extensions	Basic	4	8:6:4:2
Wrist curl	Isolation	4	8:6:4:2
Calf-raises	Basic	6	15

To further intensify your power training use even lower sets and reps.

(E.g.   5 × 6:5:4:3:2   or   3 × 5:3:2)

Occasionally you can try for a single maximum rep, using a reliable training partner to assist you, in order to assess your strength development.

DEVELOPING A 'TRAINING INSTINCT'

Use your body as a constant experiment, observing how it reacts to different stimuli of all kinds, exercises as well as diet. Note down the results in your training diary. Become more and more finely tuned to ways in which your body works. All this experience will eventually add up and provide a total picture of your development and improvement over a period of time. It will represent a vital source of personalized information.

If you compete, keep particularly detailed notes of your preparation since you will only ever learn how to reach peak condition on target by knowing exactly what you did, how you did it, and how long it took, when you eventually got things right.

Detailed 'bio-feedback' is absolutely vital for a bodybuilder and you should be aware of, and react to, such factors as the following:

1 What produces a good 'pump', when the muscle feels tight with blood after a successful exercise.
2 How you stimulate a growth spurt, or pass a training plateau.

3 What causes a noticeable increase or decrease in bodyfat levels or appetite.
4 What causes chronic fatigue, soreness or pains and how to avoid them.

The most important aspect of all to monitor is which exercises work for you, and which do not. If your back responds to lat. pulldowns, but not so well to bentover rows, then be sure to use the former exercise and reject the latter. Always select the exercises which you can feel working, and which produce noticeable results, and bear in mind that these may change periodically. Variety is the spice of training as well as life.

It may take you a long time to develop a really reliable training instinct but it is invaluable if you can and gives you a real 'edge' over your rivals. You will no longer waste time on certain kinds of training which leads nowhere, but can concentrate instead on ways which maximize your potential and get fast results.

MOTIVATION

My major training inspiration is provided by competing. I know that at least twice a year I must be in tip-top shape to stand on stage in a bikini before a critical audience and not disgrace myself. It is a pity that more women do not have to face the same ordeal; if so, then many more would be in better shape! In my case, fear of failure is the key. I find that in the off-season, my motivation is just about sufficient to get me to the gym, put in a serviceable work-out, and eat reasonably well. However, the additional effort and application required for a pre-competitive cycle is of a very different order. There comes a point where total dedication has to take over – a commitment to put in many hours, virtually every day for weeks without fail, in order to get the required results. I am sure I am not alone in finding this incredibly hard. For the pre-competitive phase, which may last 8 to 10 weeks, bodybuilding has to come first and last as your priority, and for a while social activities, domestic chores and breaks away from home all have to be forgotten.

My method of psyching-up for this all-out effort consists, first of all, in immersing myself in the bodybuilding scene. I attend a contest or two and look at the other girls against whom I may be competing. If they look good then I immediately feel spurred on! Looking through back copies of muscle magazines helps as does visualizing myself in an international line-up standing next to a top star. I look through some of my old photograph albums, or training diaries charting my own progress, or I talk to other competitors about their training. Soon, an overall picture starts to emerge. I replan my week to include a daily jog or abs. training session, and start to cut back on my food intake.

Motivation is the key and, once you have it, nothing can stop you. If you set your sights high then you will eventually get there, maybe in small steps, but you can do it. Learning the technique of psyching-up to get through one work-out that you do not really want to do, will lead to you acquiring the determination to force your mind and body to greater achievements, not only in bodybuilding but in everything you do. You must believe in your ability to progress and have total confidence in attaining the image you have created of yourself.

Do not ever let yourself become complacent or self-satisfied because however much you have achieved there is always room for improvement – there is always someone better than you are or who has the potential to beat you. Even if you do not compete, you can continually improve on your condition – there is never a cut-off point at which you attain perfection. Once you are in good shape, you will want to maintain it by continued application.

For competitive bodybuilders the quickest way to defeat is to imagine you know everything there is to know, and have a closed mind. You need to experiment, question others, read all you can and continuously learn, since only you can work out for yourself how your unique body reacts to diet and training. Other people can only give you guidelines. The most relentless questioners and experimenters are the top champions, who are never satisfied with their shape or performance.

VISUALIZATION

Visualization is a sophisticated technique of mental rehearsal which is used by many advanced athletes as an aid in reaching their training goals and advancing performance. It can be used to increase confidence, speed up the learning process, change bad habits or improve consistency.

Like any physical skill, the ability to create strong mental images has to be learned and practised regularly to be of any use. Visualization of a physical action or an emotional state can affect your physical reality. It is even possible to alter blood pressure, body temperature, heartbeat and a variety of other involuntary bodily functions.

The relevance to a bodybuilder is that you can programme your subconscious mind to anticipate certain changes in your physique, or to motivate yourself to diet and exercise regularly, or to win a championship. Once you have convinced your subconscious of the reality of the aim, you can and will actually bring it about. As one famous

bodybuilder put it, 'What can be believed can be achieved'.

A good time to practise this technique regularly is at bedtime, when your mind is relaxed and it is quiet and peaceful. You should imagine yourself vividly as you intend to look and behave in detail. Go through your training routine and imagine the exercises making your muscles grow and change shape; visualize your posing routine for a contest, move by move. Think about winning, holding the trophy and going on to win other more important contests. Do this for ten minutes every day and make a positive effort to cut out all negative visual thinking at all times.

Use the technique in the gym too, prior to each exercise; mentally rehearse it in your head and concentrate on pushing yourself to the limits.

Needless to say, this kind of 'self-actualization' can be applied in any area of life. Anyone who wants something badly enough generally achieves it. That is, in effect, practical visualization at work, though the individual may not realize it. If you consciously apply the technique, you can use your mind as your most powerful bodypart. The mind is so strong it can will your body and your personality into becoming what you want them to be. Eventually, the wish will become the woman.

BOREDOM AND STICKING POINTS

There are times when everyone feels the need for some outside stimulus to improve their mental attitude towards training. If you are visiting the gym several times each week all year round, seeing the same people and performing the same old routine, you will inevitably become bored and stale.

If your mind gets fed up then your body will cease to make progress. This may result in a sticking point when, for a matter of weeks or months, you do not seem to make any progress. The body does not develop at a regular pace and in the course of training you are bound to experience some training spurts and then longer plateaux.

Changing Your Routine

One way to combat this situation is to shock the body into new growth by completely changing your training programme. You should not follow an exercise routine for so long that the muscles become used to it and cease to react. Different exercises will affect the muscles differently and stimulate further growth. If you have been training very heavily for a long time, a period of light work-outs with high reps for a week or two can induce a renewed response and stimulate the muscles to make more gains.

Your work-outs may be too long but not intense enough. In this case, limit yourself to one hour in the gym, working to capacity. Really push yourself hard and use some intensifying techniques. If your work-outs are too intense, you will need to cut back on your work schedule and rest more.

Change your routine regularly, so that the body is always unaware of what to expect. Some people need to do this every six weeks, others find that they make better gains by training instinctively, without a pre-determined programme, simply by concentrating on the feel of the individual work-out. Everything depends on your temperament. You may be a person who responds best to routine or one who reacts better to constant variety and experimentation, but if you regularly vary your routine your muscles never become fully adjusted to a consistent pattern of contraction and they may well continue to grow in response to unfamiliar stresses.

Changing Your Environment

I find it helpful to refresh my mental attitude by training in different places from time to time. While maintaining a subscription to a regular gym, I also occasionally visit at least four others for individual work-outs. This has several advantages: you have a wider choice of equipment at your disposal and you have a chance to work in seclusion, with extra concentration. I find this especially valuable during a pre-competition phase when I need extra stimulus.

If you always train with free weights, try a few Nautilus work-outs instead for a week or two, or else leave the weights alone and go running for a week.

OVERTRAINING

If you are feeling hopelessly stale and none of the approaches described in the previous section seem to help, then you are certainly overtraining.

If you train every day, or work a muscle group too frequently, then you will never allow it sufficient recovery time to grow. Localized overtraining will fail to produce growth. In fact, you may lose muscle size by continually breaking down muscle tissue. You can appear smooth and flat, as if you haven't trained at all.

In general, at least for a novice, each muscle group requires 48 to 72 hours to recuperate and grow before it is worked again. Some muscles recover faster than this and others more slowly. For instance, the abdominal muscles recover quickly, so it is quite possible to train them daily, but the spinal erector muscles of the back are really slow to recover and should not be worked heavily more than once each week.

Localized overtraining of a muscle will slow down your progress, but general all-round overtraining can bring it to a dead halt. Classic symptoms of overtraining are:

1 Loss of interest in working-out and boredom.
2 Chronic fatigue, general lethargy, lack of concentration, irritability.
3 Susceptibility to injury, sore muscles and joints.
4 Frequent minor ailments, colds or flu.
5 Bad skin and tummy upsets.
6 Lack of progress, especially loss of muscle bulk and smoothing out.
7 Elevated morning pulse rate and poor recovery of pulse after exercise.

If you experience any or all of these, take a week off completely, and do not return to the gym until you feel better.

Overtraining is usually caused by one or a combination of the following:

1 Beginners' over-enthusiasm.
2 Work-outs too long, but not intense enough, or too many intense work-outs.
3 Insufficient carbohydrate in the diet to provide energy and protect protein for muscle building.
4 Not enough rest.
5 Vitamin/mineral deficiency.
6 Pre-contest training and dieting which is too intensive, especially if it is left too late.

Try to isolate the factors which have caused your overtraining, note them in your training diary and avoid them in the future.

ADVANCED SPLIT ROUTINES FOR PRE-COMPETITION TRAINING

The schedules which follow are designed for two purposes: the pre-competition period and, in general, to intensify training at the advanced level.

A word of warning here. *More* is not *better* in bodybuilding, *less* often is. Do not be misled into supposing that by employing an advanced schedule too soon you will progress more rapidly. It will have exactly the opposite effect and will merely induce weight-loss and overtraining if introduced early in your career, or at the wrong time in the training season.

Use the five- and six-day splits for pre-competitive phases, or for a limited period, then revert to the standard four-day split as your basic training schedule.

The Five-Day Split System

This system provides an advance from the four-day split, and is primarily useful as a transitional schedule leading to a high-intensity pre-competitive training phase. It can also be used by advanced bodybuilders for a more intense, regular training schedule.

As this system involves reduced rest periods, it should not be used by anyone who has been training for less than two years, otherwise it will lead to overtraining.

The body is divided into halves, in the same way as with the four-day split. Here is how a five-day split works through a two-week period:

	Mon	Tues	Wed	Thurs	Fri	Sat	Sun
Week 1	A	B	A	B	A	Rest	Rest
Week 2	B	A	B	A	B	Rest	Rest

Use the bodypart divisions and exercise programme as for the four-day split.

The Six-Day Split

This is primarily used for pre-contest preparation work, for 6 to 8 weeks beforehand. Advanced bodybuilders, with a highly adapted metabolism, can make good off-season progress using a six-day system, but most women training at a lower level would never make gains with so little rest.

Probably the best training system for an advanced bodybuilder to follow is three days of training followed by one day's rest on a continuing basis as described below in 1b. This is the training programme I follow and which has provided my best progress.

There are two variations of the six-day split:

1 Split the body into three sections and train each section twice a week. (A = Legs and Biceps, B = Chest and Back, C = Shoulders and Triceps, but Abs. and Calves daily.) This can be done in two ways.

System 1	Mon	Tues	Wed	Thurs	Fri	Sat	Sun
	A	B	C	A	B	C	Rest

OR

System 2	Mon	Tues	Wed	Thurs	Fri	Sat	Sun
Week 1	A	B	C	Rest	A	B	C
Week 2	Rest	A	B	C	Rest	A	B

Here is a specimen six-day split schedule, using System 1(a). (Body in three sections, training each twice per week.)

ADVANCED LEVEL SIX-DAY SPLIT (PART 1)
Purpose: Pre-competitive Schedule
(System 1)

Mon/Thurs   5-minute warm-up

Bodypart	Exercise	Type	Sets	Total Sets Per Bodypart	Reps
Abs.	Crunches	Isolation	4		25
	Off-bench Leg-Raise	Basic	4	12	25
	Twists	Isolation	4		100
Legs	Squats	Basic	4		12–15
	Leg Extensions	Isolation	3	13	12–15
	Leg Curls	Isolation	3		12–15
	Lunges	Isolation	3		12–15
Biceps	Concentration Curl	Isolation	3	6	10–12
	Cable Curls	Isolation	3		10–12
Forearms	Reverse Curls	Basic	3	3	8–10
Calves	Calf-Raises	Basic	6	6	15

ADVANCED LEVEL SIX-DAY SPLIT (PART 2)
Purpose: Pre-competitive Schedule
(System 1)

Tues/Fri   5-minute warm-up

Bodypart	Exercise	Type	Sets	Total Sets Per Bodypart	Reps
Abs.	Incline Sit-Ups	Basic	4		25
	Jack-Knives	Isolation	4	12	20
	Twists	Isolation	4		100
Chest	Dumb-bell Incline Press	Basic	4		8–10
	Flat Flyes	Isolation	3	10	10–12
	Incline Flyes	Isolation	3		10–12
Upper Back	Single Arm Dumb-Bell Row	Basic	4		8–10
	Front Lat. Pull-Down	Isolation	3	10	10–12
	Pull-overs	Isolation	3		10–12
Lower Back	Hyperextensions	Isolation	3	3	12–15
Calves	Calf-Raises	Basic	6	6	15

ADVANCED LEVEL SIX-DAY SPLIT (PART 3)					
Purpose: Pre-competitive Schedule					
(System 1)					
Wed/Sat 5-minute warm-up					
Bodypart	Exercise	Type	Sets	Total Sets Per Bodypart	Reps
Abs.	Crunches	Isolation	4		25
	Off-bench Leg-Raise	Basic	4	12	25
	Twists	Isolation	4		100
Shoulders	Dumb-Bell Press	Basic	3	6	8–10
	Shrugs	Isolation	3		10–12
Delts.	Front Raise	Isolation	3		10–12
	Side Lateral Raise	Isolation	3	9	10–12
	Bentover Lateral Raise	Isolation	3		10–12
Triceps	Single Arm Extensions	Isolation	3	6	10–12
	Pulley Pushdowns	Isolation	3		10–12
Calves	Calf-Raises	Isolation	6	6	15

Alternative System 2: Six-Day Split

Divide the body into two sections and train each three times a week. Use the bodypart divisions as for the four-day split. This is the most intense six-day system:

Mon	Tues	Wed	Thurs	Fri	Sat	Sun
A	B	A	B	A	B	Rest

On the opposite page is a *pre-competitive six-day split base* System 2 (body in two sections, training each three times per week). *N.B.* You can use either of the two bodypart division systems as described in the section on four-day splits. This specimen schedule uses the 'push and pull' system. Read carefully the notes on 'Pre-Contest Training Cycle Principles' before you start (p. 138) and apply them to this programme. Avoid using machines for all exercises in pre-competition schedules. If you wish to include supersets, trisets or giant sets you will need to rearrange the order of exercises. Refer to p. 101 for guidance.

ADVANCED LEVEL SIX-DAY SPLIT (PART 1)

Purpose: Pre-competitive Schedule
(System 2)

Mon/Wed/Fri   5-minute warm-up

Bodypart	Exercise	Type	Sets	Total Sets Per Bodypart	Reps
Abs.	Incline Sit-Ups	Basic	6		25
	Off-Bench Leg-Raise	Basic	6	18	25
	Twists	Isolation	6		100
Chest	Incline Dumb-Bell Press	Basic	4		10–12
	Flat Flyes	Isolation	4	12	10–12
	Incline Flyes	Isolation	4		10–12
Shoulders	Dumb-Bell Shoulder Press	Basic	4		10–12
	Front Raise	Isolation	4		10–12
	Side Laterals	Isolation	4	16	10–12
	Bentover Laterals	Isolation	4		10–12
Triceps	Behind Neck Single Arm Triceps Extensions	Isolation	4		10–12
	Pulley Pushdowns	Isolation	4	8	10–12
Calves	Calf-Raises	Isolation	6	6	15

ADVANCED LEVEL SIX-DAY SPLIT (PART 2)

Purpose: Pre-competitive Schedule
(System 2)

Tues/Thurs/Sat   5-minute warm-up

Bodypart	Exercise	Type	Sets	Total Sets Per Bodypart	Reps
Abs.	Crunches	Isolation	4		25
	Jack-Knives	Isolation	4	14	25
	Twists	Isolation	6		100
Legs	Squats	Basic	4		12–15
	Leg Extensions	Isolation	4		12–15
	Leg Curls	Isolation	4	16	12–15
	Lunges	Isolation	4		12–15
Upper Back	Dumb-Bell Bentover Row	Basic	4		10–12
	Lat. Pulldowns	Isolation	4	12	10–12
	Cross-Bench Pull-over	Isolation	4		10–12
Lower Back	Hyperextensions	Isolation	3	3	15
Biceps	Preacher Curls	Basic	3	6	10–12
	Cable Curls	Isolation	3		10–12
Calves	Calf-Raises	Basic	6	6	15

THE DOUBLE SPLIT SYSTEM

This is an extremely intense pre-competition
training system which should be used only for the
last 2 to 3 weeks prior to a contest. This system is
especially demanding, because it coincides with the
period when energy levels due to dieting are at their
lowest ebb, and daily aerobic work is at its most
intense. For these reasons, the body requires to be in
a highly adapted state to benefit from a double split.
I would not recommend this training system, except
for the most advanced competitors at national or
international level.

Another point to consider is that it takes a major
investment of time. If you have a full-time job, then
it would be very hard to train in this way.

There are two variations, one more intense than
the other.

1.	*Morning*	train major muscles
	Evening	train abs. and calves
2.	*Morning*	complete work-out (a)
	Evening	complete work-out (b)

Using this split, you can train either:

1 Two major work-outs, three days weekly, plus one
  major work-out on alternate days.
OR
2 Two major work-outs for six days, plus one day's
  rest.

I once tried a double split for one week, prior to the
1983 British Championships, and ended up badly
overtrained – flat, smooth and exhausted. I was
simply not experienced enough at the time to cope.
More haste, less speed! So, do not attempt it, unless
you are ready to take on some very classy opposition
and know you have the background stamina and
grit to survive.

Chapter Seven

NUTRITION FOR BODYBUILDING

INTRODUCTION

Good nutrition is a vital part of the battle to achieve a superb physique, and it is the key ingredient in any health and fitness programme. However much effort may be concentrated on training, no athlete will achieve his/her maximum potential unless their diet is also carefully planned. Nobody expects a high-performance car-engine to run on cheap fuel, yet that is precisely what most people expect of their bodies.

It is very likely that your diet could be much improved to provide your body with the type of high-quality fuel which will help it to remain healthy and energetic throughout your life. For any athlete in training, this is doubly necessary. Your body will be subjected to a great deal of additional stress, both mental and physical, during a heavy work-out, and the right diet is needed to help your tissues recover fast, repair, grow and then be ready for the next session.

Because we live in an industrialized society with ready access to convenience foods of all kinds, it is very easy to be sedentary, overfed, and undernourished. The hopelessly unbalanced Western diet, loaded with fat, sugar and salt, insidiously piles on the weight, sludges up the body systems with toxins, clogs up the arteries and causes listlessness, depression and endless minor ailments. We accept as normal a generally low level of health and vitality mainly because the majority of people have forgotten how it feels to be healthy and full of vigour. It is a feeling most people have not experienced since they were about sixteen years old and is not simply a question of not being noticeably ill but is an awareness of having unlimited physical and mental energy and a calm well-adjusted approach to life. If you are fit, you can cope with everything in your life far more easily, without becoming overwrought, exhausted or depressed. Your stress levels are reduced, and you can deal with a greater workload or busier life without your

body or mind breaking down.

To make matters worse, to overcome the general debility and high stress levels we experience, we indulge in stimulants and depressants to keep us going. Not just one, but a whole cocktail: alcohol, coffee, tea, cigarettes, chocolates, cola drinks, drugs of all kinds. Most of these are regarded by the body as poisons and dealt with accordingly. As we may absorb many of them daily, we tend to increase the quantity over a period of time to achieve the same effect, and our bodies simply cannot cope.

Most people assume that they are already eating a 'balanced diet'. By 'balanced' I mean the recommended amounts of nutrients, vitamins and minerals daily. When you consider that the average diet consists very largely of processed foods, overcooked and reheated canteen or restaurant meals and a very limited range of favourite foodstuffs, it is easy to see that most people are not eating a balanced diet at all. Far too much of the wrong kind of food is consumed. If you are overweight and over-eating, you are suffering from malnutrition as surely as someone who is underweight. The body has to take in a vast excess of 'junk' food in order to extract a sufficient amount of the essential nutrients it needs to survive. In doing so, it also takes in an excess of fat and simple sugars which are stored in the body, causing overweight. Most of our foods are de-vitalized before we buy them, they are packaged, canned, frozen, pre-cooked, dehydrated, bottled or dried. During their preparation they have sugars, salt, colourings, preservatives, flavour enhancers and emulsifiers added. In some cases, synthetic vitamins are added, to compensate for the natural ones lost in processing. Even fresh foods are not always what they may seem. Oranges sometimes have no vitamin C in them; factory farmed eggs may contain very little protein, fruit is treated with pesticides, and colours and perfumes are sprayed on prior to sale to make it look and smell good. Our meat is injected with antibiotics and steroids; some blue cheeses have even been injected with penicillin.

Eating in Western society can very definitely be hazardous to the health! As the years pass, we ingest an amazing concentration of harmful chemical substances with which our bodies find it hard to cope. Actually, it is remarkable how well they do, considering the amount they are neglected.

It is obvious that radical changes should be made and gradually people are becoming more aware of this. In the USA, there has been a highly successful national campaign to improve the nation's diet and exercise levels. This has resulted in a dramatic decrease in the amount of heart disease and an all-round improvement in health and therefore work performance. Unfortunately, there will always be many vested interests within the food industry, which will continue to promote basically unhealthy products so, as individuals, we need to stay constantly alert and stick to our nutritional principles, since our lives depend on it.

DIETS AND EXERCISE – THE PROBLEMS

If you are overweight and decide to go on a diet to reduce your bodyfat, you must be very careful about the way you do it, since it could eventually lead to you becoming fatter than ever. This is especially true of the type of 'crash' diet which guarantees a dramatic weight loss in a short time. The only way to lose bodyfat effectively and permanently is very slowly.

Bodybuilding is concerned with reducing bodyfat to the lowest possible level, while building up muscle tissue at the same time. Male bodybuilders have been doing this very effectively for the past thirty years, and their superb physiques demonstrate how successful their methods are. Now that women are bodybuilding too, exactly the same principles are being applied by them.

The average healthy woman who is not overweight carries about twenty-five percent bodyfat. Many women carry a great deal more. A woman bodybuilder strives to maintain a bodyfat level of about twelve to fifteen percent, reducing it further for contests. The fact that top women have appeared in contests with bodyfat levels as low as four percent proves that it can be done, and healthily, and that bodybuilders know a thing or two about how to manipulate nutrition for their own purposes, without sacrificing appearance.

Many of the principles of bodybuilding nutrition established over the years are now being recognized as having a more general application. Because of the demands of the sport, a great deal of research has been carried out into methods of maintaining muscle and losing bodyfat at the same time.

The Diet/Binge Cycle and Its Effects

Dieting alone will not work. You will start with a fat, flabby body, and end up with a thin, scrawny one, in exactly the same proportions as you started. When you diet, you not only lose bodyfat. At first, you lose a great deal of water, as you cut back on carbohydrates, which retain water, then you lose bodyfat plus muscle tissue. The ratio can be as much as one lb of muscle to every two lbs of bodyfat. The more drastic the diet, the more muscle will be lost. In contrast, a long-term gradual weight-loss programme, aiming to lose only one to two lbs weekly, minimizes the amount of muscle lost.

The loss of muscle is a critical factor. Muscle tissue burns calories even while you are resting, but fat is inert. In other words, the more muscular you are, the more energy you consume just ticking over, so a fit, muscular person can actually eat more and gain less fat weight than someone who is overweight and out-of-shape. If you crash diet and lose muscle, and later revert to your old eating habits, you may easily regain all the weight you have lost – but not the same type of weight. What you put back will not be fat and muscle, but only fat. So you may have lost five lbs of fat and two-and-a-half lbs of muscle, but regained seven-and-a-half lbs of fat alone. If you then crash diet again later on, and keep repeating this diet/binge cycle, the end product over a period of years will be a very much higher bodyfat percentage than at the start.

Another problem associated with crash diets is that the brain is alerted by the sudden reduction in food intake to expect a famine. It does not know that you are dieting, so it assumes you are starving and reacts appropriately by trying to conserve its energy supplies. This triggers off very powerful enzymes which encourage fat storage. In this situation, muscle tissue will be called upon preferentially before fat stores, to supply your energy. This spells disaster for a bodybuilder.

Another sneaky trick the body plays during a diet is to lower the metabolic rate – the rate at which energy is used by the body. If you are trying to lose weight, this is self-defeating. What is worse, if you diet repeatedly, the metabolic rate will gradually reduce to a point where the amount of calories you use is so minimal that the slightest amount of extra food will pile on weight and no amount of dieting, however stringent, will work. This is frequently what happens in the case of middle-aged women who eat practically nothing but still cannot lose weight.

It is now known that the body has a built-in

appetite-regulating device, which has been nicknamed the '*appestat*'. In a fit, healthy person, this acts as a control mechanism. It might be supposed that energetic exercise might increase the appetite, but this is not the case – in fact, it decreases it. But it appears that the '*appestat*' is only effective if you are fit and exercise regularly. It rapidly becomes ineffective if you have a sluggish lifestyle. The result is that a sedentary person loses touch with his/her nutritional requirements, and is inclined to eat habitually to satiation point. As his/her abdominal muscles are probably also slack and flabby, the stomach is able to expand without restriction to accommodate the extra quantity, and gives none of the right signals to stop.

In a fit person, the body is self-regulating. It demands the appropriate nutrients in the correct quantities to maintain performance, and then calls a halt. In addition, tight stomach muscles act as an in-built corset and prevent unlimited expansion. A feeling of fullness comes much faster as the stomach contents meet the pressure of the hard abdominal wall.

The important thing when dieting is to lose slowly, in combination with aerobic exercise, which raises the metabolic rate at the same time. Over a long period, your body will accept a lower level of fat storage as normal, and you will remain lean.

Cellulite

A great deal has been written on the subject of 'cellulite' – the fat deposits which collect primarily on the lower body in women, with the lumpy appearance of orange peel. A whole industry was built up to help women lose 'cellulite' by passive methods, wired-up to machines, wrapped up in foil, and so on. 'Cellulite' is just plain old fat, nothing more, deposited due to a poor basic diet.

The lumpy fat deposits of 'cellulite' are no respecters of age; you can have them around your lower body at eighteen or fifty-eight even if you are reasonably lean in the upper body, and they are certainly tough to remove. The only sure way to do so is by a combination of good nutrition, exercise and patience, which is what this book is all about.

Toxins

Because our diets are generally so poor and overloaded with additives, our bloodstreams and tissues habitually have to cope with a great many toxic substances. These can gradually accumulate in our organs (e.g. heavy metals like lead, mercury and arsenic from exhaust fumes, atmospheric pollution, mercury from contaminated tuna fish), and under the skin in the fat storage areas.

We are all composed of chemicals of course, together with a large amount of water, but our systems were not designed to cope with the sheer concentration of poisons we now ingest. Struggling to cope, our body has to operate at a much lower level of performance. If we treat ourselves like rubbish bins, that is the way we will look and feel.

Excuses

Here are some of the most common excuses given by the overweight. 'I have big bones.' (Nobody's bones weigh more than 14 lbs, whatever their height or size.) 'I have water retention.' (If you retain water to any great extent, it could be a very serious medical problem, so see a doctor.) 'My family were all overweight, so it is hereditary.' (Your family all had bad eating habits, probably instilled by mother or grandmother, or whoever controlled the cooking.) 'I like my food.' (Don't we all! But good health is much more enjoyable.) 'I've tried every kind of diet, but never lose weight.' (Then try exercise and write down the calories of everything you eat to see how much self-deception you are practising.)

Unless you have a really serious metabolic imbalance, *you* can be slim and fit. It just takes self-discipline and time but *nobody* is incapable of improving what they have.

HOW TO MAKE DIETARY CHANGES

After years of bad dietary habits, it would be too much of a shock for the body to change your diet overnight to a completely new and different system. You would not feel better at all, just queasy and upset. The secret is to introduce changes gradually, to understand the principles of proper nutrition and to work towards the optimum diet for you. You should not regard your new eating plan as a 'diet' at all, rather as a new way of eating for the rest of your life. Do not regard it just as a short-term weight loss programme to be followed by a reversion to your old eating pattern after a few weeks. You need to change the eating habits which made you fat, gradually and permanently, and to be critical about everything that goes into your mouth. Inevitably that will mean giving up some types of food altogether. But really persist, until you reach the point where a sugary snack, over-salted food or fatty meat all physically repel you. That is the way to stay lean for life, with flawless skin.

Read as many articles and books on the subject as you can but do it critically. Most women's magazines these days are full of nutritional advice and if you read around the subject, you will be able to experiment until you find out what suits you. No one can recommend the ideal means of losing weight for you personally, or the type of foods which will suit your system best. Both are intensely personal and what works for one person will be quite wrong for another. You will have to find out the details for yourself.

Buy yourself a calorie counter. You need to know automatically the calorific values of most main foods. Look up all your regular favourites, and make a personal reference list. You may get quite a shock. You should be aware of the calories you are taking in. For example, did you realize that a glass of orange juice has the same number of calories as a glass of white wine? Egg white is 10 calories, egg yolk is 70 calories, though each contains 3 grams of high-class protein. So it is obviously better to eat the whites than the yolks from a slimming and health viewpoint. Give the yolks, whipped in milk, to your cat, who will thrive on them.

As far as nutrition is concerned the more knowledgeable you are, the more likely you will be to maintain a stable weight and a healthy diet and to know what to do if you start to gain or lose weight. This information is crucial for anyone who is responsible for feeding others, since bad nutritional habits are taught in the home, and once adopted are very hard to eradicate.

Get back in touch with your body and listen to it. Learn to recognize the signs of real hunger and do not eat until you experience them. If you are not hungry then do not eat, even if it is supposed to be a mealtime. On the other hand, do not skip meals so that you become ravenously hungry and then binge. If you feel really sluggish, give your system a rest and have a day of fruit, salad and vegetables only.

The body requires a fairly consistent intake of food throughout the day, in order to keep the blood sugar level stable, giving you plenty of energy and fewer hunger pangs. It is much happier operating on little and often than on a starve/binge cycle as it provides more stimulus to the metabolic rate. Your system can absorb about 20 to 30 grams (about 4 ozs) of protein at one sitting and any excess will be stored as fat, so try to divide up your protein intake during the day. If you want to eat 225 g (about 8 ozs) of meat, eat it in two helpings at two different meals.

The worst pattern of eating is to skip breakfast, skip lunch and rely on one heavy main meal. Overnight you probably fast for twelve hours from 8.00 P.M. to 8.00 A.M. In the morning your system needs protein for tissue repair. The usual breakfast is high in sugary carbohydrates and low in protein. If you eat fish, meat, egg or cheese for breakfast, it will prevent you feeling hungry for a sweet snack at 11.00 A.M. and give you a better start to the day. The traditional type of breakfast eaten in the last century, with mutton chops or kidneys and bacon was much better nutritionally than our sugared cornflakes, toast and butter and marmalade!

How To Start

Go through your store cupboard and fridge critically and throw away all the processed junk. The only canned product I buy is tinned fish, which is generally not full of rubbish. (Unfortunately, we do not yet have salt-free products of this kind, as in the USA.)

Decide to buy only those foodstuffs which will be good for you. Do not bring anything else into the house. You can be certain that if it is there, you will eventually eat it. Seek low-calorie alternatives for your usual foods, such as skimmed milk for whole milk, Outline or St Ivel Gold for margarine or butter, cider vinegar and lemon juice instead of oil/vinegar salad dressing, low-fat live yogurt for sweetened varieties. If you have a meal out, or a weekend at home with your mum, then go straight back to your normal eating pattern afterwards. You should aim at eating properly at least seventy-five percent of the time, even if you can't be perfect.

Individualizing the Diet

As you become a more experienced bodybuilder and competitor, you will come to realize more and more that both training and diet are very individual. The more information you obtain by picking other people's brains, or reading books and magazines, the more you must also learn to sift critically, to experiment, and to retain what is right for you and reject the rest.

I have found, for instance, that for me a high-protein diet is not only indigestible and toxic, but it actually curtails my progress and doesn't build muscle. Some people will need high protein, but others will fare better on low protein, high carbohydrate. If you are vegetarian, too, you will need to be even more careful if you want to make gains.

Basically you should follow your instinct. If you feel bad on one type of food, try another until you feel fit and energetic. Eliminate anything which saps your energy level. Seek out a formula which guarantees you gains, and if it stops working adapt it as necessary.

Ask yourself the following questions about any new food you introduce:

1 Does it give you more energy for a work-out?
2 Does it help you recuperate quickly?
3 Does it leave you feeling energetic or sluggish?
4 Does it help you sleep better?
5 Do you achieve good definition by eating it before a contest?
6 Does it keep your skin clear and healthy looking?
7 How does it affect your gut?
8 How does it affect your emotions?

By keeping a detailed record of such information, you will soon develop your instinct to a high pitch and establish what is right for you. Everyone has a unique metabolism and reacts differently to various foods. What works for one person will not work for another. You may be vegetarian or hate tuna fish, or be allergic to some fruits and vegetables. It is just a question of finding out all you can about yourself, how you react, and then adapting it to your personal requirements. Keep careful notes, so next time you compete you can follow the method of cutting-up (see glossary) that's proved most successful for you and not repeat old mistakes.

Allergy Testing

A great many people are now beginning to realize that they are allergic to certain foods and that their symptoms are not just caused by a late night, high relative humidity or imagination. I am convinced that the epidemic of allergies we now hear so much about is because we have all been raised on a remorseless diet of chemical additives, preservatives, artificial colourings and flavourings, all of which accumulate in our system and catch up with us sooner or later.

Whatever the cause, the aim of the nutritionist must surely be a diagnosis of each person's individual sensitivities, and the planning of a personal diet to suit them. Bodybuilders already attempt this, but even they may be unaware of existing allergy problems which can seriously affect their ability to metabolize food into energy, and by implication to build muscle. Your progress can be brought to a dead halt by undetected allergic reactions.

If you suffer any of the following symptoms, you may well have an allergy:

■ General persistent listlessness and depression.
■ Unexplained fatigue.
■ Catarrh.
■ Wind and stomach pains after eating.
■ Nausea after eating.
■ Temporary improvement in symptoms after eating, but feeling worse later.
■ Headaches and migraine.
■ Water retention or bloated stomach after meals.
■ Dizziness.
■ Skin troubles.
■ Addiction to certain favourite foods.

The symptoms can be much worse than these.

If you think you may be a sufferer, it is really worthwhile having an allergy test carried out by a reputable clinic. It may cost a little, but will not be money wasted. You will be put on a detoxifying diet intended to flush the allergens from your system. This may take a week or so, and during this time you may feel quite unwell, but at the end of the week, you will suddenly feel immeasurably better and almost a new person.

Allergic substances act rather like drugs – we are usually addicted to the things to which we are allergic. As you continually top up the level of toxic material in your body, you obtain temporary relief from the symptoms. Later on, you will feel much worse, until you eat more of the same substance.

If you eat a large amount of one food every day, your system can develop an allergy to it. Bodybuilders, for instance, need to watch out for allergies to chicken, tuna, eggs, milk, brewer's yeast, bran, wheat products, and so on. In time, with treatment, you may be able to develop a tolerance and re-introduce the allergens in small quantities. Once you have stopped eating them for some time, you will notice a much more pronounced reaction if you are unwise enough to sample a forbidden food.

I recently had an allergy test and found I was allergic to practically everything I ate regularly, including all the bodybuilder's standard foods such as chicken, tuna, eggs, soya, and gluten. No wonder I felt so bad! My revised diet has made a vast improvement in my general health, digestion and ability to build muscle. I would urge anyone who has a problem to have a similar analysis, and act on the advice given, however sceptical you may be at first.

THE COMPOSITION OF FOOD

All foods contain a mixture of nutrients in varying proportions. Very few are pure sources of one type alone. The principal food components are proteins, carbohydrates and fats, together with vitamins and minerals.

Protein is used by the body first and foremost for repair and growth. It is therefore of primary importance to any athlete or bodybuilder.

Proteins are made up of hundreds of amino acids, of which only twenty-two are used by the body. Only nine of these are essential. They are histidine, isoleucine, leucine, lysine, methionine, phenylalanine, threonine, tryptophan and valine. The non-essential amino acids are manufactured by the body from any excess of the essential ones, as and when they are needed.

All proteins from animal sources are 'complete' or 'first class'. That is to say, they contain all nine essential amino acids together in a form which is readily assimilated and utilized by the body. As the essential amino acids cannot be synthesized in the body, they must be derived from the food we eat, and they must all be ingested together. If only one amino acid of the essential nine is missing, then it is impossible for the body to utilize any of the protein eaten. The highest amino acid content of all is contained in egg whites, followed by milk, red meats, fish and poultry.

Foods which contain only some of the amino acids are called 'incomplete' or 'second class' proteins and these must be eaten in combination with another complementary food, to make up the deficiency. This is the fundamental basis of a vegetarian diet, since soya and sprouted seeds are the only complete vegetable proteins. Grains, nuts, beans and seeds, etc., are all incomplete proteins. However, when eaten in certain traditional combinations, they convert to first-class proteins. Many Third World countries rely on such traditional combinations for their protein sources, which are in no way inferior to animal proteins.

The principal combinations to create complete vegetable proteins are:

1 Seeds and beans and peas (e.g. houmous, which is a combination of chickpeas and sesame seeds).
2 Grains and milk (e.g. rice pudding).
3 Grains and beans and peas (e.g. beans on toast).

Mixtures of animal and vegetable proteins such as bread and cheese, egg and potato, fish and chips, chilli con carne, pizza and paella are all high in protein value (though for a bodybuilder, many are too high in fat).

Protein for Growth, Repair and Energy

Protein intake will rarely match the requirements of the body exactly, for growth and repair – there is bound to be either an excess or a deficit. The body can absorb about 20 to 30 grams of protein at one sitting for direct use in body maintenance and growth. Any excess beyond this level is wasted, because it will not be used for building muscle, but instead will be converted into glucose for energy by a lengthy and inefficient process.

For a bodybuilder, the amount of protein consumed and the way in which it is eaten can make all the difference between gaining quality muscle, and making little progress, regardless of hard training.

For the average sedentary person, the recommended daily protein intake is ½ to 1 gram per kilo of bodyweight. Bodybuilders in training probably need twice as much. Many women eat too little protein, especially of the right kind, and their lack of muscularity may be directly related.

How Much Protein and How Often?

First of all, calculate how much your protein intake should be.

My off-season bodyweight is usually about 120 lbs and I estimate that my protein intake should be between 1 to 1½ grams per kilo (2 lbs). I have trouble digesting protein, and find a daily intake of about 60 grams ideal for me. I divide this up into four feedings of 15 grams, which is well within the maximum amount recommended for effective tissue repair and growth, and does not involve ingesting any excess. This is on the low side for a bodybuilder, but it suits me. Any more and I feel sludged up, queasy and lethargic.

If I opted for the higher level I should either need to supplement my four meals with two or three protein powder shakes daily, or have several further small meals.

In order to work out the protein content of standard foods, you must have a chart such as the *Manual of Nutrition*, published by HMSO, which will give you the protein, carbohydrate and fat content of all standard foods, as well as calorific values, vitamin and mineral contents.

So if you wish to gain muscular bodyweight, eat protein in small quantities, frequently throughout the day. The body is then able to continue its work of growth and repair with a steady intake of the necessary nutrients, without having to deal with any excess. It is particularly important to ensure that you have a good-quality source of protein at breakfast time, after the normal all-night fast.

Too much protein, however, can be very damaging to your health, and will put a great strain on your kidneys. If you are a bodybuilder you have probably experienced at one time or another the heavy, sludged-up feeling caused by excessive protein intake. The kidneys fail to function properly and the excess of toxic substances produced circulates in the bloodstream, causing unpleasant side effects such as constipation, excessive wind and bad breath, queasiness and lack of appetite. I have experienced 'protein poisoning' and it is very unpleasant. For a bodybuilder, it is self-defeating. If you eat expensive protein hoping to build muscle but cannot absorb it, you succeed only in making yourself feel bad and limit your progress. You will need to experiment to find out how much protein you can take in comfortably.

To help digest protein, you can take a supplement of betain hydrochloride (HCL) with each meal, or other digestive enzymes such as papaya, pepsin, etc.

Protecting Your Protein Intake

The latest thinking in bodybuilding nutrition advises a moderate consumption of protein, combined with a high complex carbohydrate intake. Since altering my own diet to this combination, I have felt much more energetic, had no unpleasant side effects, and made rapid gains. It is altogether a much healthier diet for anybody but it has a very important significance for bodybuilders.

The body needs a sufficient supply of protein to do its repair work, before it starts to build muscle but protein cannot be metabolized properly except in the presence of carbohydrates. If the carbohydrate intake is too low, then the body will use its protein supplies for energy instead. If the protein intake is too low, then the supply of amino acids for muscle growth will be inadequate and no growth can occur. If the carbohydrate level is critically low (for instance, on a very low carbohydrate diet) then the body will be forced to steal protein from the muscles themselves for energy, since protein is not stored anywhere else in the body for emergency use, like fat. The resultant loss of muscularity is obviously disastrous for a bodybuilder. In other words, carbohydrates spare protein and therefore muscle. If the complex carbohydrate level is kept high, then all the protein absorbed can be used first of all for maintenance and, more important to a bodybuilder, tissue growth.

Sources of Protein

A bodybuilder should pay close attention to her protein sources and ensure they contain high-class combinations of amino acids. They must also be low in fat and therefore calories. This considerably restricts the available sources, cutting out red meat, oily fish, full fat cheese and other dairy products, egg yolks, and whole milk, nuts and seeds. Obviously, in the off-season, some of these can be eaten occasionally with no ill-effects, and should be, to maintain a balanced diet. But in general terms, for good health, high fat proteins are best avoided. The best protein sources for bodybuilders are white fish, poultry, cottage cheese, low-fat yogurt, skimmed milk, egg whites and protein powder supplements, soya and sprouted seeds.

Good bodybuilding food combinations which fulfil all requirements are jacket potato and cottage cheese, wholemeal bread and tuna fish, brown rice and chicken, low-fat yogurt and fruit. These are all high protein, high complex carbohydrate and low-fat combinations.

Protein supplement drinks are often recommended for bodybuilders seeking to gain bodyweight, and they also make a quick meal if you are in a hurry. An egg and milk protein combination is the best-quality source available because of its high biological value. It is general practice to drink these supplements between meals because they would be wasted if added to a meal containing the maximum assimilable amount of protein.

I prefer to derive my protein from natural sources, and find both soya-based protein powder, and egg and milk protein cause indigestion, wind and bloating. This may be an allergic reaction. (This also applies to soya products like tofu and textured protein.) If you can tolerate them, they are good for rapid weight-gain, and for anyone who needs to increase their protein intake considerably. Bodybuilders should anyway stop taking protein supplements when preparing for a contest, since they normally contain excessive sodium.

Sources of protein are as follows:

Animal	Meat, poultry, fish, cheese, eggs, milk, protein powder, yogurt.
Vegetable	Soya products, sprouted seeds, potatoes, peas, pulses, nuts, dates, wholemeal bread and flour, cereals, vegetarian protein powder, spirulina

Vegetarian Bodybuilders

Some top champions are vegetarians, but it is not easy for them to obtain sufficient high-quality protein. It is doubly important if you are a vegetarian to ensure that your knowledge of which foodstuffs to combine is accurate. Many vegetarian protein sources are not only bulky and indigestible and so converted very slowly and inefficiently by the body but are incomplete proteins and therefore not properly assimilated.

The amount of protein in nuts, seeds and pulses is very high, the same as in meat, fish and cheese, provided they are eaten with the correct complementary foods, but they are all high in fat too. Cereals (wheat, maize, rice) are also high and potatoes are a good source. Most other vegetables are low.

Bear in mind that cereals and pulses are also high in complex carbohydrates. This is beneficial as a protein-protector, but they are also bulky to eat in quantity and will distend your stomach. Pulses can cause severe wind in people who lack the necessary enzymes in their gut to digest them properly, and the fibre in the grains can be highly allergenic, causing water retention and bloating. If you can possibly bring yourself to eat fish, milk or eggs then do so. If not, supplement your diet with a good vegetarian protein powder.

Carbohydrates

Carbohydrates are the body's preferred energy source. They are very simply metabolized (unlike protein), and are the best quick fuel source for the expenditure of effort, for instance, a heavy work-out.

There are three main groups of carbohydrate in foods. These are:

1 Sugars
2 Starches
3 Cellulose and other fibres known as 'roughage'.

Each type of carbohydrate is converted to glucose (blood sugar) in the body at a different speed. Simple sugars convert to energy in the bloodstream almost at once, starches take longer and roughage is not absorbed at all, but simply passes through the body, aiding digestion.

Excess carbohydrates in the form of glucose are converted to fatty acids or triglycerides which are then stored in the body. In simple terms, if you eat too many carbohydrates you will get fat.

The consumption of carbohydrates protects protein in the body from being used as fuel (as described in the previous section), and allows it to be used for growth. Bodybuilders should therefore *never* cut out carbohydrates completely, however rigorously they diet.

Carbohydrates are also essential for efficient fat metabolism. In their absence, fat breaks down into ketones, which can lead eventually to a sodium imbalance and dehydration.

You should eat at least 150 grams of carbohydrate daily (1 gram = 4 calories. Refer to a good carb. counter booklet such as the *Manual of Nutrition*.) Seventy-five grams will be utilized for basic metabolic functions, and the remainder for energy. The main metabolic requirement is for the working of the brain, which runs almost entirely on carbohydrate, in the form of glucose. This is why, if you go on a low, or nil carbohydrate diet, your blood sugar levels will be low and you will be sleepy, unable to concentrate and lethargic, since your body will conserve every scrap of carbohydrate energy to keep the brain functioning.

Carbohydrates, as their name implies, attract water. If you cut them out of a diet you will see a dramatic drop in weight during the first few days as the water associated with them is lost. However, the body needs carbohydrates to function and it will strive to retain its normal carbohydrate level. The result is that following a prolonged period of low carbohydrate dieting you will develop an irresistible craving for them. The sudden uncontrolled intake of carbohydrates in these circumstances is very bad for you. First of all, it causes massive water retention, and secondly a dramatically elevated blood-sugar level. If you really go mad, you could, in these circumstances, go into an insulin coma. Another thing it does is to cause a rapid gain in fat weight very fast indeed, since excess carbohydrates, beyond your energy requirements, are immediately converted to bodyfat and stored.

Sugars (Monosaccharides)

All sugars are 'simple' carbohydrates and are of no nutritional value to the body, other than for energy production. Simple sugars are metabolized very fast and while being a source of quick energy, this is of a very short-term kind. When you take in refined sugar, in a form which is far more concentrated than ever occurs in nature, your system reacts by producing insulin to clear out the excess. In a healthy person this process is so efficient that too much sugar is removed and the blood sugar level becomes too low. The result is that you will experience fatigue, depression, irritability, nervous tension, stress, and a craving for more sugar to raise the level to its former high, when you felt energetic. This condition, following the initial quick 'high' is known as 'sugar-shock'.

If you eat a sugary breakfast or lunch, this is how you will feel about two hours later – say at 11.00 A.M. or 3.00 P.M. Do you recognize your mid-morning or teatime symptoms? This may lead you to eat a sweet biscuit or doughnut with a sugary drink at such times. By lunchtime or evening, your symptoms return and the cycle is repeated through the day. Your metabolism and your emotions are on a seesaw. You can stop this cycle by giving up simple sugars completely.

Simple carbohydrate sugars include glucose, glucose syrup, fructose (a natural sugar found in fruit, vegetables and honey), sucrose (found naturally in sugar cane and beet, carrots and some fruits, but mainly in the form of refined sugar), maltose, and lactose in milk (though many adults lack the enzyme necessary to digest the latter).

High concentrations of simple carbohydrates occur in alcohol, white refined flour and every product with sugar added in any of the forms listed above. If you read the labels on packets and cans, you will soon discover that they frequently contain two, three or more different sugar sources, which constitute a main ingredient of what are popularly known as 'junk foods'.

Except for fructose, they all cause 'sugar-shock' and in excess are extremely detrimental to health, causing tooth decay, diabetes, obesity and heart and bowel diseases. They are not far short of smoking as a health hazard.

Because the average diet contains so much processed food, the average intake of simple carbohydrates is far too high. It is not enough to stop taking sugar in your tea. Sugar is *everywhere*. I have even noticed it added to a well-known brand of tinned lamb stew babyfood.

Sugar would only occur in a natural wholefood diet in minute quantities (fructose in fruit and honey, lactose in milk), and then only in the proportions nature intended, not concentrated and refined.

If your intake of simple carbohydrates is too high, you will know where it goes when you look sadly at your thighs, backside and hips in the mirror.

Starches or Complex Carbohydrates (Polysaccharides)

As far as carbohydrates are concerned, these ones are the 'good guys'.

Plants form sugars in their leaves and store them in their stems and roots as starch, and thereby provide us with a prime source of complex carbohydrates. Bodybuilders should derive their carbohydrates at all times from this source, and only in small amounts from sugars (and these should only be the natural sugars, fructose and lactose).

Complex carbohydrates are digested much more slowly than sugars, so they are more satisfying to eat and they release energy slowly into the bloodstream, without causing any energy imbalance. For this reason they are an ideal source of steady energy for a work-out. A jacket potato will give you far more stamina than, say, fruit or a sugary snack.

Main Sources of Complex Carbs.	Wholegrain cereals (e.g. wheat, maize, barley, oats, millet, rye, buckwheat, rice, etc.), wholemeal flour, potatoes, vegetables, beans of all kinds and peas.
Main Sources of Simple Carbs.	Refined sugar (sucrose) and anything containing it (e.g. almost everything processed, tinned, packaged, instant mix, frozen, bottled, etc.). Natural fructose sugar in honey, fruit, (very high in grapes) and some vegetables such as carrots. Lactose (in milk). Glucose and glucose syrup. Maltose in (fermenting) alcohol.

Glycogen is similar in composition to starch, but is manufactured in the body from glucose ingested from external sources, such as fruit, honey and complex carbohydrates. Only small amounts can be stored in the liver and muscles as an energy reserve. This level can be artificially raised by athletes who require long-term energy (e.g. marathon runners), by 'glycogen loading' (see p. 146).

Specific simple carbohydrate foods to avoid:
Cakes, biscuits, sweets, bottled fruit juices and other 'junk' drinks, concentrated natural fruit juice, alcohol, honey, molasses, highly sugared 'health' foods such as muesli, processed breakfast cereals and cereal bars, chocolate, maple syrup, ice cream, jams, syrups.

Cellulose and other 'Roughage'

This occurs in the fibrous structure of vegetables, fruits and cereals. It is insoluble and cannot be digested by man, so it passes straight through the body. Many vegetables are so fibrous, particularly if eaten raw, that they actually use more energy to digest than they provide. Eating plenty of roughage will fill you up and decrease your appetite, adding bulk to the faeces and aiding digestion. It is of great importance to the health of the digestive system. Constipation is generally caused by too much protein and not enough roughage of this type.

If you have a high protein diet and insufficient roughage this can lead to a build-up of toxic wastes in the gut, and ultimately might cause cancer of the colon, a relatively common diet-induced disease in the Western world.

Too much roughage in the diet, on the other hand, can lead to bloating, flatulence, and poor protein absorption. However, few people eat enough fibre to cause these problems.

Sources of roughage: Green leafy vegetables, salad vegetables such as celery, lettuce and broccoli, fruit, bran cereals.

Fats

Fats are the most concentrated source of energy, providing 9 calories per gram compared with 4 calories in protein or carbohydrate. They represent the main energy store for all animals, in the form of bodyfat.

Because fats are digested slowly, they are satisfying, filling to eat, and a long-lasting source of energy. They suppress the appetite and prevent you feeling hungry again quickly.

Chemically, fats consist of mixtures of triglycerides, each triglyceride being a combination of three fatty acids. Dozens of these occur in nature. They sub-divide into:

a. Saturated fatty acids which are hard at room temperature (e.g. meat fat, butter, lard, suet, margarine, coconut oils).

b. Polyunsaturated fatty acids which are liquid at room temperature (e.g. olive oil, fish oils and vegetable seed oils).

Some forms are called 'essential fatty acids' because they are required in small quantities for normal health (two to three percent of your total intake).

Polyunsaturated fats, including fish oils, are beneficial in the diet in limited amounts, but saturated fats in excess are strongly linked with degenerative heart disease.

Uses of Fat in the Body

1 As an energy reserve.
2 Padding for the main internal organs (essential bodyfat).
3 Insulation to maintain body temperature and protect against extremes of heat and cold.
4 Maintenance of healthy nerve function.
5 Essential for the absorption and storage of fat-soluble vitamins.
6 In women, characteristic fat storage areas are associated with the erogenous zones and give us the curves which are a part of our sexual signalling system.

For bodybuilders, reducing the ratio of fat to muscle in the body is all-important, and even more so prior to a contest. Because the average Western diet is grossly overloaded with fat, it would benefit anyone, bodybuilder or not, to change to a low-fat diet for the sake of good health. It is not necessary, or advisable, to cut out all fat all the time. Some fat is necessary for the reasons listed above. The idea is to keep fat levels as low as possible and prevent excessive fat build-up.

Your own body-type critically influences this process and so will the amount of exercise you take. If you store fat easily, you should keep your intake low at all times. If you have a fast metabolic rate, and burn it off quickly, then you can afford to take in rather more.

Athletes of any kind will be hampered by too much bodyfat, which produces unwanted stress on the heart and circulation, impedes movement and causes excess body heat.

For competing bodybuilders, even a relatively small amount of bodyfat will conceal muscular 'definition', and so stores need to be kept as low as possible all year round in order that pre-contest dieting need not be too rigorous. A reasonable off-season level might be 15 to 20 percent, reducing to 10 to 14 percent for a contest. Although some top professionals claim to achieve levels as low as 4 percent, I cannot believe that this is healthy in the long term, since it is below the body's basic fat level needed to carry out its essential functions. For most women, a normal bodyfat level of 20 to 25 percent is ideal to keep them looking trim and curvy. If it creeps any higher then cut back on your fats. Remember, it is not how much you weigh that matters, but the critical ratio of bodyfat to muscle. This is what makes you look either terrific or terrible.

You can have your bodyfat percentage measured with calipers. If you belong to a really good gym, they will have the equipment and expertise to monitor you on a regular basis. You should take advantage of this facility.

Sources of Fats

Animal Sources	Fatty fish, poultry, meat, full fat milk, cheese, egg yolk, dairy products, ice cream, lard and dripping, shortening, cream and cream substitutes.
Vegetable Sources	Margarine, cooking and salad oils, nuts, bread, flour, seeds, pulses, oatmeal, avocados, corn, bananas.

To Summarize:
If energy is deficient in the diet, for instance from a limited intake of fats and carbohydrates, the body will use its protein supplies instead. It will then not have enough left for growth and maintenance.

This is very important for bodybuilders to know because it means that:

1 A steady supply of first-class protein is essential throughout the day to stimulate growth.
2 Complex carbohydrates must be kept high if you are on a low-fat diet.
3 Fats must be kept high on a low-carbohydrate diet.

GENERAL DIETARY PRINCIPLES FOR HEALTH AND FITNESS

1 The kind of diet to aim for is one in which all your **foods are as natural as possible.** If you can imagine that you had to produce your own food, without the benefit of modern chemical sprays and fertilizers, then you would probably have to limit yourself to vegetables, fruit, dairy products, meat and fish, all of it uncontaminated by processing and the addition of excessive amounts of sugar, salt and preservatives. Much of its nutritional value would be intact, since vegetables and fruit would be freshly picked and organically grown and livestock would be raised without drugs.

2 **Eat as much of your vegetables and fruit in as raw a state as you can.** You will eat less in a raw form, since it is bulkier and takes longer to chew, and all the vitamins which cooking destroys will be preserved. You will also take in complex carbohydrates, roughage and fruit sugars in the proportions that nature intended, not in concentrations that upset the digestion and pile on bodyfat due to excess calorie intake.

3 **Limit the amount of fat that you eat**, especially animal fat. Never fry anything. Cut out cooking oils, olive oil, salad dressings and mayonnaise. Avoid high-fat dairy products such as hard cheeses, butter, margarine, whole milk, whole yogurt, egg yolks. Substitute cottage cheese, skimmed milk, low-fat yogurt, egg whites, low-fat spreads (such as Outline or St Ivel Gold). Avoid avocados.

4 **Cut down or give up red meat.** It is loaded with fat, even with the visible fat trimmed away. If you must eat it, choose lamb in preference to pork or beef, trim off all visible fat and cook well. Always grill meat or bake on a wire rack so that the fat drips off, then throw the juices away, don't use them to make gravy or sauce. Eat liver once each week. Skin duck, chicken and turkey before cooking. Eat more white meat and fish. Avoid oily fish (e.g herrings, kippers, mackerels, sardines in oil), and choose cod, haddock, halibut, plaice, trout or prawns instead.

5 **Eat a reasonable amount of roughage** in the form of wholemeal bread, brown rice, unsalted rice cakes, raw vegetables and fruit, wholemeal pasta, pulses, and obviously don't add butter or oil. Don't overdo it. These are all high in carbohydrate and are therefore fattening in excess. A very high roughage diet may give you a distended stomach, wind and discomfort, as well as inhibiting the efficient absorption of protein and calcium. These are all bad news for bodybuilders.

6 **Eat as wide a range of foods each week as possible.** Be adventurous and try a few things you do not normally eat. The reason for this is that each individual type of food has different combinations of essential nutrients in it. If you eat a wide variety of foods, you will stand a good chance of eating an optimally balanced diet.

7 **Read the labels on packets and tins critically.** If you see sugar or salt listed, do not buy the product. Remember that ingredients on a label are listed in order of their quantity in the product. For example, 'sugar, blackberries, sucrose, pectin, glucose syrup, preservatives, permitted colouring' – is jam with three kinds of sugar in it and plenty of other junk besides.

8 **Restrict the amount of grains, milk and dairy products that you eat.** Approximately fifty-five percent of people are allergic to them and, among other symptoms, allergies cause inflammation which can lead to massive water retention. This will give you a bloated 'puffy' appearance. If you are allergic to bread, eating only two slices can retain water weighing 7 lbs.

9 **Avoid stimulants** such as coffee, tea, alcohol, chocolate, colas. Choose herb tea, mineral water (sodium free), china tea, decaffeinated coffee, an occasional glass of dry white wine, diluted fruit juices. Competitive bodybuilders, in the last stages of pre-contest preparation, drink only water – distilled is best, since tapwater contains sodium.

10 **Cut back on salt (sodium) intake** at all times. Don't put any on the table or add it to your food and gradually phase it out of your cooking. Avoid products with high salt content (e.g. packaged soups, soda water, salted nuts, smoked foods, cheese, artificial sweeteners). Sodium is a poison to the system, and most people take in about twenty times more than they need every day. The body requires such a small amount to function that enough is provided in one serving of fresh green vegetables (without salt added, of course).

The body retains water to dilute the salt you take in, so the more salt you ingest, the more water you retain – and that could mean pints. One gram of sodium will retain 50 grams of water in your body for two or three days. It is now recognized that excess salt intake is one of the major imbalances in our diets, and can cause high blood pressure leading to heart disease. So for the sake of your health and your figure, give it up. Food tastes a lot better without it once you are used to it, and you will soon find salted food unpalatable, if not actually inedible. If you really *have* to use something, try a low-sodium, potassium-based salt substitute, obtainable from any chemist. It is, however, much better to start using a variety of herbs, lemon juice and natural spices to flavour your food.

Bodybuilders need to remember that sodium is also present in many natural foods and in order to obtain contest definition it is not enough to watch salt intake just in cooking or on the table. Many of the culprits are popular natural foods for bodybuilders. Buy a copy of *The Salt Counter* (Pan Books, 1984) for guidance.

11 Eat only natural complex carbohydrates for your energy source and avoid all processed simple sugars.

Obtain your energy from complex carbohydrates. Instead of eating a pastry loaded with refined sugar, fat and white flour, eat a jacket potato or wholemeal bread (though watch out for the commercial ones that contain sugar in several forms), a plate of plain brown rice or pasta, sun-dried fruit, a few nuts and raisins or fresh vegetables and fruit. Cut out biscuits, cakes, ice cream – all the junk which is sludging up your system. Don't just take my word for it – try it, and see how much better you feel in only a few days.

Fresh fruit and dried fruit contain sugar, but it is natural fruit sugar (fructose), not refined sugar (sucrose, etc.). It is present in its natural proportions, plus roughage. Avoid fruit juices which concentrate fructose and therefore calories. Fruit sugar does not have the same effect on the body as sucrose and does not cause 'sugar-shock', unless highly concentrated.

12 If you are overweight, reduce your daily intake of food by 10 or 12 percent until your bodyfat is reduced to the level you require. Eat sensibly according to these rules and eat smaller portions. Eat little and often to keep up your metabolic rate and burn off more calories.

13 If you are underweight take in plenty of protein, plus protein supplement drinks. Cut out aerobic exercise, and rest as much as you can.

14 Protein intake. Protein is vital to every bodybuilder since it provides the building blocks for the body. Eat low-fat protein at regular intervals, in small quantities throughout the day for maximum benefit in building new muscle tissue. Make sure you eat protein at breakfast time in particular.

15 Remember that *whatever* food you eat, if your daily dietary intake exceeds your energy output then you will store the excess as fat and gain weight. It makes no difference whether it is fat, carbohydrates, protein, high fibre, 'health' food or

alcohol and black coffee, the end result will be a fat backside and thighs.

The only way to lose weight and stay slim is to be highly selective and to stop putting fattening things into your mouth, on a regular basis. The minute that your waistbands grip tight, it is time for action.

DIETING TIPS

1 Really listen to what it is that your body requires. It may not be food at all; it may need a drink, it may need rest. If you know that you eat too much at particular times of day, or under stress, or when you are unhappy, then try to avoid situations which encourage you to over-eat. Change your environment and habits to trick yourself.

2 Make your meals a ritual, take time and trouble over presenting them. Be sure you have peace and relaxation.

3 A glass of wine may be relaxing but it will also weaken your willpower, so only have it if you know you can resist food later.

4 Eat your meals from a small plate, so that you seem to be eating more. The idea in the long run is to shrink your stomach. It is only an expanding bag and if you train it to expect less it will decrease in size and then you will feel full more quickly.

5 Divide your meals up into several small snacks during the day and never over-eat. Keep your calorie intake the same though, just divide the same quantity into more feedings.

The hardest exercise anyone ever learns is to push themselves away from the table.

SUPPLEMENTATION

Why take supplements at all?

It is hard enough to balance your diet knowledgeably and efficiently in order to extract the basic nutrients in sufficient quantities, but it is virtually impossible for athletes who place extraordinary demands on their bodies.

Exercise burns up the calories but at the same time it stresses every bodily system, especially the glands, causing a greater demand for additional vitamins, minerals and other nutrients. In order to help the body to cope there has to be a calculated adjustment. In the case of a runner or swimmer, food

intake can be increased to much higher levels to supply extra nutrients, since much of the excess will be burned off aerobically. For a powerlifter, shot-putter or javelin thrower power, not appearance, is vital. But for a bodybuilder who seeks high energy reserves, stamina, quick recovery and muscle growth, all in combination with low bodyfat, it is no use relying solely on natural food sources. It is essential to use the aid of supplements which will provide high levels of quality nutrients in easily assimilated, concentrated form, without overloading the digestive system or encouraging the deposition of unwanted bodyfat.

One extremely good reason for taking supplements, even if you are not an athlete, is that the average diet contains so many processed, packaged and otherwise devitalized foods that however careful you are, it is nowadays practically impossible to achieve a healthy balanced diet. (This is, by definition, one which supplies the basic nutrients in sufficient quantities.) Most people do not know what the basic nutrients comprise, let alone the quantities they require, or how to obtain them. In view of these factors, extra vitamins and minerals are a worthwhile insurance policy for your continuing health.

What Do They Do?

Supplements are used by bodybuilders for three specific purposes:

1 To help build new tissue.
2 To repair tissue fast and efficiently after a work-out and to speed up recovery time.
3 To prepare the body for the next work-out and sustain it at a high energy level.

They take four main forms:

1 Vitamins
2 Minerals
3 Protein
4 Miscellaneous other helpful natural substances

The whole subject of supplementation is a minefield for the beginner and it is easy to get carried away into spending a great deal of money unnecessarily. Bodybuilders probably excrete the most expensive urine in the world!

Always remember, supplements are an aid. They are never a short-cut method of building a great physique. You can only achieve that aim by training consistently hard over a long period of time.

Vitamins

The most important supplements of all are combinations of the various vitamins. Vitamins are a twentieth-century discovery and the first one was identified in 1911. Many others have been isolated since then and their importance to our health and well-being has been established as fundamental. Vitamin C, for instance, was not chemically produced until 1933, although it had been used, without realizing exactly what it was, since the eighteenth century by the British Navy, in the form of limes on board ship to cure scurvy. Carrots have been used since Roman times to cure night-blindness, due to their high carotene content (Vitamin A).

Vitamins are essential to life itself and are not just a fancy addition to the diet of health-food fanatics. For athletes of all kinds they are vital in enhancing performance, energy levels, stamina, recovery, and maintaining a high level of general health and resistance to infection.

General vitamin deficiencies manifest themselves as listlessness, debility, lack of growth and depression. Severe deficiencies can cause a wide range of serious illnesses.

There are two types of vitamins, water-soluble ones (B complex and C), and fat-soluble ones (A, D, E, K). Excess water-soluble vitamins are excreted in the urine but excess fat-soluble vitamins accumulate in bodyfat and can be toxic.

The B-complex vitamins act in relation to one another in the body. In combination, they are responsible for maintaining mental health, the health of the nervous system, the digestion and the skin. They are the 'anti-stress' vitamins. As they act together, any supplement of one B vitamin should always be accompanied by another, containing the rest of the complex. No B vitamin can work in isolation. They are all water-soluble, and are not stored for long in the body, so they need to be taken daily.

The following charts should give you an idea of what vitamins are all about and help you to select the ones which will benefit you most.

Vitamin	Scientific Name	What it Does	Sources	Deficiency Causes	Recommended Daily Dose	Fat/Water Soluble	Remarks
A	Retinol	Growth, healthy skin, good eyesight.	Fish liver oils, offal, dairy products, carrots, green vegetables, margarine, butter, milk, eggs.	Lowered resistance to infection, skin complaints, night-blindness.	2500 i.u. (Britain) 5000 i.u. (USA)	Fat. 90% of bodily reserves are stored in the liver.	Toxic in high doses. Some food sources contain carotene, which can easily be converted to Vitamin A in the body (carrots, apricots, green vegetables).
B Complex							
B$_1$	Thiamin	Necessary for the maintenance of nerves, digestion and muscle growth; metabolism of carbohydrate into energy; growth.	Yeast, wheatgerm, milk, cereals, offal, eggs, pork, whole grains, pulses, sea food.	Exhaustion, depression, poor digestion, nervous complaints. *Severe:* beri-beri	1 mg per 1000 calories	Water.	Acts in combination with the rest of the B Complex vitamins.
B$_2$	Riboflavin	Growth; metabolism of energy from protein; healthy skin and eyes; general health.	Milk, yeast, liver, green vegetables, meat, eggs, cheese.	Common deficiencies include skin ailments, poor nerves, dry hair, lack of stamina, light sensitivity.	1.3–1.7 mg	Water.	Destroyed by ultra-violet light (e.g. if milk is left on doorstep all day).
B$_3$	Niacin *or* Nicotinic Acid	Brain function; utilizing energy from food; enzyme production.	Liver, meat, bread, milk, fish, vegetables, yeast, peanuts.	Tension, depression. *Severe:* pellagra.	15–18 mg (Britain) 20 mg (USA)	Water.	Antibiotics can cause deficiency.
B$_5$	Pantothenic Acid	Tissue growth, healthy skin and hair.	Wholemeal bread, brown rice, eggs, nuts, liver, yeast.	Dry hair and skin.	5–10 mg	Water.	
B$_6$	Pyroxidine	Balances body chemistry; metabolizes protein; forms haemoglobin, which transports oxygen in the blood to the muscles; increases energy; helps prevent bloating, by balancing fluids in the system.	Bran, wheatgerm, wholegrains, liver, yeast, brown rice, fish, oats, milk, cabbage, bananas, avocados.	Depression, irritability, muscle cramps, skin ailments, insomnia, weight loss.	1 mg (Britain) 2 mg (USA)	Water.	Deficiency often caused by the contraceptive pill. A high protein diet requires extra B$_6$ to aid metabolism. Useful as a slimming aid as diuretic.
B$_{12}$	Cyanocobalamine	Involved with folic acid in the formation of red blood cells; helps to give more energy and endurance; involved in protein metabolism; helps maintain healthy nerves.	Liver, egg yolks, cheese, milk, meat, fish.	Digestive and nervous problems, skin ailments. *Severe:* pernicious anaemia	1–5 mcg (Britain) 10–15 mcg (USA)	Water.	Can be stored in the liver for up to 3 years, but is destroyed by light. Does not occur in vegetable sources, so vegetarians need to take a supplement. Some bodybuilders believe B$_{12}$ injections to be beneficial. These can cause scarring if used regularly.

Vitamin	Scientific Name	What it Does	Sources	Deficiency Causes	Recommended Daily Dose	Fat/Water Soluble	Remarks
B Group	Biotin	Health of muscles, nerves and skin.	Liver, kidney, oats, eggs, nuts, wheatgerm.	Eczema, hair-loss, possibly impairs control of cholesterol levels.	1 mcg	Water.	
B Group	Choline	Essential for liver function; speeds up metabolism of bodyfat.	Soya, sunflower seeds, egg yolks, liver, yeast, oats, nuts, wheatgerm, wholegrains.	Liver disorders, reduced alcohol tolerance.	10 mg (Intake of choline should be twice that of inositol.)	Water.	Taken by bodybuilders to help 'cut-up' for contests. A useful slimming aid.
B Group	Folic Acid	Growth, brain function; acts with B_{12} in formation of new red blood cells; fertility.	Raw green vegetables, liver, kidney, yeast, soya, wheatgerm, wholegrains, lentils. Also produced in the intestines.	Depression, weakness, anaemia. *Severe:* Megaloblastic anaemia.	0.5 mg (Britain) 400 mg (USA)	Water.	90% is destroyed by cooking. Action is impeded by alcohol and birth pills.
B Group	Inositol	Liver function; in combination with choline, helps to lower cholesterol levels, and aids in fat metabolism; affects muscle and skin tissues.	Liver, yeast, soya, sunflower seeds, wheatgerm, oatmeal, molasses, fresh fruit.	Liver disorders, reduced alcohol tolerance.	10 mg (Intake should be half that of choline.) (Normal diet provides up to 1000 mg daily.)	Water.	Mostly concentrated in the body in the heart, muscles, eyes and brain.
B Group	Niacin (Nicotinic Acid)	Growth, nerves, healthy skin; digestion of carbohydrates.	Meat, fish, wholegrains, peanuts.	Skin ailments, poor nerves, stomach upsets, insomnia, headaches.	15–18 mg	Water.	
B Group	Para-Amino-Benzoic Acid (P.A.B.A.)	Keeps body functions regular, in combination with rest of B-Complex.	Milk, yeast, liver, eggs, wheatgerm.			Water	

NB DO NOT TAKE SUPPLEMENTS OF VITAMIN B AND VITAMIN C TOGETHER AT THE SAME TIME OF DAY. THEY WILL CANCEL EACH OTHER OUT.

Vitamin	Scientific Name	What it Does	Sources	Deficiency Causes	Recommended Daily Dose	Fat/Water Soluble	Remarks
C	Ascorbic Acid	Maintenance of healthy connective tissue and muscles; helps in the absorption of iron; acts as a de-toxicant; in megadoses can clear the system of toxic substances (e.g. heavy metal accumulation such as mercury and lead, and cancer-forming nitrites found in food preservatives). Helps fight allergies; combats infection; megadoses now help to prevent colds; aids recuperation; forms red blood cells.	Acerola cherries, oranges, rosehips, blackcurrants, green and red peppers, potatoes, sprouted seeds (½ cup = 6 glasses of orange juice).	Tissue breakdown leading to bleeding and scurvy; sore gums; lowered resistance to infection, joint pain, slow healing.	30 mg (Britain) 50 mg (USA) 120 mg (USSR) Dr Linus Pauling = 1–2 grms.	Water.	Not stored in the body. Extremely unstable. Vitamin C is damaged by light, heat, water, keeping food hot. Deficiency can be caused by smoking, stress, some drugs, a diet high in processed foods. Man is one of the few animals unable to synthesize Vitamin C in the body, so it has to be derived from the diet. Most animals keep their Vitamin C levels at saturation point.

Vitamin	Scientific Name	What it Does	Sources	Deficiency Causes	Recommended Daily Dose	Fat/Water Soluble	Remarks
C (Cont.)							Some fresh foods do not contain Vitamin C as they should due to prolonged storage. Any excess is excreted in urine – a natural diuretic. Always occurs in nature in combination with bioflavonoids.
D	—	Healthy skin and hair condition; used for bone and teeth formation; calcium and phosphorus cannot be absorbed without it. Assists in energy release in the body; builds muscle strength.	Eggs, butter, oily fish, margarine, dried milk powder. Mainly manufactured by the body from exposure of the skin to sunlight. Fair skins produce more than dark.	Weak muscles, retarded growth, tooth decay. Severe: Rickets.	100 i.u.	Fat	Toxic in excess (over 1000 daily i.u.) should be ingested in combination with fats or oils, or as a fish oil supplement.
E	Tocopherol (D-Alpha is best)	Fertility and muscle health. Functions not fully understood but thought to include the following: enables the blood to transport oxygen more efficiently = (extra endurance). Improves recovery speed and muscle function. Anti-oxidant, which protects polyunsaturated fats from being destroyed by oxygen in the body. Protects Vitamin A, carotene, and the sex and pituitary hormones. Relieves angina, thrombosis and heart disease by decreasing the body's need for oxygen. Dilates blood vessels improving circulation. Megadoses can improve virility. Protects lungs from air pollution. Reduces side effects of pain-killing drugs. Applied externally, helps repair and heal scar tissue, stretch marks, wrinkles and burns. Relieves menopausal symptoms.	Wheatgerm, oil, unprocessed vegetable oils, wholegrain cereals, nuts, egg yolks, wholemeal bread.	Weak muscles, cramp, deterioration of red cells, nervous complaints. Infertility (in animals).	100 i.u. can be built up gradually to 600+ i.u. daily	Fat	Take with a meal containing oil or fat. Iron destroys Vitamin E, so do not take these two supplements in combination. An increased amount is required in a diet high in polyunsaturated fats. Destroyed by food processing.

Vitamin	Scientific Name	What it Does	Sources	Deficiency Causes	Recommended Daily Dose	Fat/Water Soluble	Remarks
K	–	Involved in chemistry of blood clotting.	Produced in the intestines. Green leafy vegetables, pith and skin of fruit and vegetables, tea, wine, beer, coffee.	Increased bleeding.	Unknown. Diet provides up to 400 mg daily.	Fat	Antibiotics can cause deficiency.
P	Bioflavonoids (Group of compounds found in plants.)	Protects Vitamin C from oxidation.					

Minerals

Fifteen minerals are known to be essential and have to be derived from food. The most important for bodybuilders are iron, calcium, zinc, phosphorus, magnesium, sodium, chlorine, potassium, iodine, chromium, copper, manganese and sulphur.

Minerals have three main functions:

1 They build up body components such as bones and teeth (calcium, phosphorus and magnesium).
2 They help to control the body's metabolic processes (e.g. sodium, chlorine, potassium, magnesium, phosphorus).
3 They are necessary for the action of enzymes, which help in the release and use of energy (e.g. iron and phosphorus).

Multi-Mineral Tablets act as a good all-round basis for mineral supplementation. People with a nutritional deficiency tend to suppose that vitamins are always the culprits. In fact, mineral deficiency is more widespread, so a supplement is important for anyone having an active lifestyle. You can have your personal mineral status determined by analysis of a hair sample (by clinics advertised in health magazines).

Mineral	Where Found in the Body	What it Does	Sources	Deficiency Causes	Recommended Daily Dose	Remarks
Iron	In red blood pigment (haemoglobin). Also in muscle protein (myoglobin) and in organs (e.g. liver).	Oxygen conveyance in the bloodstream. Helps raise energy levels. Component of enzymes required to fight infection.	Liver, kidneys, dried apricots, watercress, bread, spinach, eggs, molasses, raisins, plums.	Anaemia: lack of energy, headaches, lowered resistance to infection, irritability.	12–18 mg daily. Menstruating women up to 25 mg daily.	Dieting may cause deficiency. Menstruation frequently causes deficiency. Essential for all athletes. Over-dosage can cause tissue damage.
Calcium	99% is in the teeth and bones – the most common mineral in the body.	Formation of teeth and bones. Ensures physiological balance. Contraction of muscles (including heart), blood-clotting, enzyme activity. Nerve transmission.	Milk, cheese, bread, eggs, sardines, watercress, cabbage, yogurt, wholegrains, nuts, seeds.	Imbalance with phosphorus, causing irritability and nervous tension. Stunted growth, bone loss in the old, rickets.	500 mg (Britain) 1000–1500 mg (USA) (Overdoses can cause kidney stones.)	Bodybuilders dieting for a contest will probably be deficient and should take a supplement. Use of diuretics will reduce calcium levels. High protein diet, carbohydrate loading and taking of thyroid and growth drugs also increase calcium loss. Added fibre in diet can reduce absorption. Has a calming effect on the nerves. Can help insomnia taken late at night.
Zinc		Hormone action. Energy production. Vitamin metabolism.	Offals, especially liver, shellfish, fish, wholegrain cereals, pulses, green vegetables.	Widespread adverse reactions in skin, hair, nails. Mental lethargy, poor appetite.	15 mg	Particularly susceptible to deficiency are those on the pill or on steroid drugs.
Phosphorus	Bone tissue. Second most abundant mineral in the body.	Strengthens bones and teeth. Helps utilize energy, enables B Vitamins to function, muscle contraction, nerve transmission, fat and carbohydrate metabolism, hormone secretion.	Nearly all foods, especially dairy products, meat, fish, wheatgerm, eggs.		1000–1500 mg (should be same as calcium to balance the two minerals).	
Magnesium	Bones.	Helps enzymes build protein. Growth, repair of body cells, muscle action, interacts with calcium. An electrolyte.	Wholegrains, nuts, pulses, dried figs and dates, seeds, grapefruit.	Upset nerves. Muscle convulsions, cramps.	150–450 mg (Britain) 300–400 mg (USA)	Diuretics may cause a deficiency. Important in endurance activities.
Sodium	In all body fluids, as sodium chloride (salt), especially the blood.	Maintains water balance in the body. Maintains muscle and nerve activity.	Processed foods, especially smoked products and cheese.	Muscular cramps, dehydration, low blood pressure. *Excess intake causes fluid retention. High blood pressure.*	4 g daily. (Excess excreted in urine.) This is present in natural foods.	Sodium attracts and retains water, so bodybuilders should eliminate it for the last week before a contest otherwise water retention will blur hard-won definition. Supplementation unnecessary. Most diets are already far too high in sodium.

Mineral	Where Found in the Body	What it Does	Sources	Deficiency Causes	Recommended Daily Dose	Remarks
Chlorine		Eliminates waste products. Production of digestive acids. Connective tissue health.	Green vegetables, seaweed, olives.			
Potassium	Total amount in body is related to the ratio of lean tissue.	Controls balance of body fluids. Complementary action with sodium. Healthy nerve function. An electrolyte conducting electrical energy around the body, especially the heart.	Apricots, bananas, fruit juice, vegetables, fish, meat, milk, cheese, grapefruit, green peppers.	Tiredness, muscle weakness, listlessness.	2–4 mg	Use of diuretics can lead to dangerous potassium deficiency, causing cramping, faints, irregular heart beats and ultimately heart failure.
Iodine		Involved with thyroid hormones which control growth and metabolic rate.	Seafood, seaweed.	Muscle weakness, slow metabolic rate, apathy, drowsiness. Severe: goitre.	200 mcg	Kelp tablets containing iodine are taken by bodybuilders who believe they speed up the metabolic rate. Any drug use may lead to a deficiency.
Chromium		Maintains normal blood levels. Lowers cholesterol levels.	Liver, wheatgerm, wholegrain cereals, shellfish.	Poor blood-sugar control.	200–290 mcg	
Copper		Transport of oxygen in bloodstream. Part of several enzymes.	Shellfish, fish, wholegrains, raisins, prunes, nuts, seeds, dried beans.	Poor resistance to infection. Diarrhoea.	2 mg	
Manganese		Blood-sugar control. Aids resistance to infection. Interacts with B-Complex vitamins. Connective tissue maintenance, growth and reproduction.	Wholegrain cereals, nuts, pulses, eggs, sunflower seeds, green leafy vegetables.	Susceptibility to infection.	2–3 mg	
Sulphur		For the health of hair, nails and skin. Vital in production of amino acids.	Eggs, fish, cabbage.	Skin irritation, weak nails, poor hair condition.		

133

Where to Buy Supplements

A good selection of supplements is readily available from most health food stores or good chemists. Be critical about the brand you buy. Many commercial vitamin and mineral supplements have comparatively low dosages, and are full of additives, sugar and useless 'fillers'. The USA-recommended daily dosages are all at least 50 percent higher than ours, so their supplements are invariably stronger. If you are sensitive, buy those which are gluten-free, or vegetarian.

Multipacks for bodybuilders are now available, which take the problems out of supplementation by providing all the different pills you need for one day in pre-packaged form. These are very good for beginners, but as you individualize your training and diet, you should also tailor your supplementation to suit your personal requirements. This is particularly necessary during the pre-competitive cycle, when the diet is restricted and nutrients cannot all be obtained from the food eaten. They are also good for off-season training but the wider range of food you consume at this time will supply most of your essential requirements.

Supplements are expensive, so bulk-buy if you can, perhaps with a group of friends. Some gyms supply a range of bodybuilding supplements at a discount. Remember that it is an investment in your health and strength – money you might once have spent on cigarettes, alcohol or rich food, all of which undermine your health.

As a general guide, here is a brief summary of some of the most popular supplements (other than vitamins and minerals), together with a brief explanation of what they are supposed to do for you.

1 Protein Powder

If you wish to increase your muscular bodyweight, then a protein powder supplement can be helpful. Personally I consider that protein is best derived from natural sources, particularly as many protein supplements have sugar and other undesirable substances added to them. However, if you find it hard to eat breakfast, or you are in a rush, a protein shake can be whipped up in a few minutes and will have the same nutritional value as a meal. Do not completely substitute protein drinks for proper balanced meals. Use them as a supplement to your normal diet (e.g. mid-morning, mid-afternoon, bedtime). Milk and egg protein is the best quality powder to buy. If you find it hard to digest milk, then try a soya-based product. Be warned that many people suffer from wind and stomach bloating after drinking this type. 'Casilan', a protein powder for invalids is nutritionally very good as is 'Bipro' (which is extracted from cheese whey and is 97 percent protein and tastes neutral). As I am allergic to eggs, milk and soya, I cannot take any of the usual protein powders. However, there is one on the market now, based entirely on white fish, called 'Ocean Powder' by Ultimate Nutrition. This is highly recommended if you are also sensitive to these foods. To mix a protein shake, use about 10 fl ozs of skimmed or raw milk, or fruit juice. Add ice cubes, fresh fruit and two tablespoons of protein powder, liquidize in a blender (a good investment for a bodybuilder). You can add anything else you like, for instance, wheatgerm, honey, molasses or you can make a savoury shake with vegetable juice and chopped fresh tomatoes, parsley or spinach.

2 Liquid Amino Acids

This is protein, broken down into its basic constituents. It is a thick brown liquid like treacle and looks and smells perfectly disgusting. It has the same effect as protein powder, in that it helps to build muscle tissue. It gives me, and everyone else I've asked about it, such bad wind that it becomes antisocial to work-out with anyone else. This seems to me to be counterproductive. Never take amino acids without a supplement of tryptophan, which is invariably deficient in most commercial brands.

3 Liver

This is available in tablet form, as desiccated liver, or in liquid form. It is a type of concentrated protein much favoured by bodybuilders, second only in nutritional value to milk and eggs. Liver not only helps to build tissue, it is also an amazing source of energy, since it encourages the release of glycogen from the liver and muscles. It is packed with B-Complex vitamins and also minerals including iron.

Try to buy Argentine liver, which is not polluted by hormone injections, and watch out for tablets that are full of sugar, chalk or other nutritionally useless binders. Some male bodybuilders take handfuls of liver tablets daily, but 6 to 12 would be ample for a woman in off-season training, spaced through the day. A few taken an hour before a work-out will really give you some extra energy. Don't take them after 6.00 P.M. or you may be too stimulated to sleep, although I imagine they may add zip to your love life!

Watch out for possible toxic reactions in the body, if you also take protein supplements regularly. You may find you are overloading your kidneys and that uric acid is polluting the bloodstream. If this happens, cut back on protein and take megadoses (3 to 6 grams or more) of Vitamin C daily to detoxify until you feel better.

4 Digestive Enzymes

If you have trouble with protein digestion, take a supplement of hydrochloric acid which should help. *Papaya* or *bromelain enzyme* tablets are also useful proteolytic enzymes and very pleasant to take.

If you are on a low carbohydrate diet, you may be short of digestive enzymes, so these will make a useful addition.

5 Kelp

This is a sea-vegetable, rich in minerals and trace-elements. It is one of the best sources of iodine, and also contains B-Complex, D, E, and K, calcium and magnesium. Some experts believe it helps speed up the metabolism, so it is frequently used by bodybuilders seeking to lose bodyfat for a contest. It is also a natural diuretic.

6 Cider Vinegar

A digestive aid and a natural diuretic which encourages weight-loss. It clears the system of bacterial build-up, and has a detoxifying effect. Take a tablespoonful in water every day for good health.

Combinations and Dosages

What you decide to take will depend on your personal requirements and your bank account. Read as much as you can on the subject, but do seek advice from an expert sport nutritionist, who will diagnose your individual needs. Listen to what other bodybuilders say about supplements they have tried and their results, but do not follow them slavishly, as is so often the case.

Experiment, learn, reject and experiment again. Keep careful notes on how you react to each new supplement you introduce. Try each one for a month at least, since many have no noticeable short-term effect. Notice if the supplement adds to your work-out energy or your muscular gains. Adjust the dosage if it does not work at first and try again.

Multivitamin Tablets

These are high-powered concentrations of a wide range of vitamins, suitable for the average person to take on a daily basis to ensure all-round good health.

Bodybuilders should take one or two daily as a foundation for all their other supplements, to ensure that nothing vital is missed. Take these tablets with your meals for the best effect.

Suggested Daily Off-Season Supplementation

Try any combination. These are in order of priority:

Megamulti-vitamin

Multi-minerals

Vitamin C

Vitamin B Complex

Vitamin E

Vitamin B6

Choline ⎫
Inositol ⎭ in combination

B12: Important for all bodybuilders, but vegetarians in particular.

Pre-contest Supplementation

Double up on all supplements if dieting heavily.
Increase kelp, cider vinegar, B6, choline and inositol to aid definition.
Magnesium and potassium will help prevent cramping.
A herbal diuretic such as Boldo or Aquatrim will help immediately prior to a contest if needed.

BODYBUILDING DRUGS

Unfortunately a whole pharmacy of drugs is used by competitive bodybuilders to achieve muscle growth and optimum appearance. Bodybuilding is infamous for drug-abuse and unless it is stamped out the sport will never become acceptable as an Olympic event. Male bodybuilders are now virtually obliged to take potentially dangerous drugs such as anabolic steroids (male hormones) in order to compete at all, simply because they are in competition with other drug-induced physiques. Many other sports are equally implicated, for instance heavy field athletics.

The main reasons why drugs will continue to be used undercover by top athletes despite the danger of discovery by mandatory drug testing at international events are that virtually everyone else uses them at the top level, and without them all records would drop back to pre-drug levels and seem pathetic in comparison.

Most bodybuilders take up their sport for health and fitness, but at some point face the dilemma that to win at the highest level almost inescapably means taking drugs. In my view, this is the point where desire for success, fame and financial rewards overcomes common sense. They risk damage to their own health, and they also cheat their more scrupulous rivals.

Experienced judges can usually spot the tell-tale signs of drug use (e.g. poor skin tone) and may mark down the competitor in question, preferring, at least in women's contests, a naturally built physique. But, unfortunately, it is not always obvious, and no one has yet devised a method of positively identifying offenders quickly and inexpensively and disqualifying them. And of course, at present there is no rule which actually bans drug use.

In this country, bodybuilding drugs are doubly dangerous since they can only be obtained on the black market and taken in ignorance. At least if they were supplied by doctors and taken under strict medical supervision it would minimize the risk of severe long-term effects. Many bodybuilding drugs are especially damaging to women. Anabolic steroids in particular induce a condition akin to male adolescence, producing severe acne, loss of normal feminine contours, masculine pattern of hair growth, deeper voice, clitoral enlargement, diarrhoea and probably in time liver and kidney damage. They can also damage the foetus. Some of these effects are irreversible.

I hope that in Britain, sensible and thoughtful women competitors have not yet experimented and never will. I would never take so much as an Aspirin for bodybuilding, if it interfered with my health and fitness. Make no mistake, drugs are dangerous, and drugs are CHEATING.

Chapter Eight

TRAINING AND DIETARY CYCLES

The basic principle of cycle-training is that the athlete alternates periods of intensive training and strict dieting with periods when she can ease the pressure of training and relax her diet. Cycle dieting is based on the nutritional requirements of the bodybuilder during three separate phases:

1 Off season training.
2 Pre-competition training.
3 Maintenance training in-season, between contests.

Most athletes now follow a year-round régime. No top athlete in any discipline these days can afford to let up at all. The competition is far too fierce, determined and high-class. If you are aiming for the top, your commitment has to be total, and that means relentless attention to your training and dietary intake all year round. In the past it may have been possible to have long lay-offs, but not any longer.

If any athlete maintained the same intense level of training all the time, they would quickly become overtrained, exhausting both their physical and mental resources. In order to cope with this problem, most competitive bodybuilders now follow a system based on training and dietary cycles. This allows them to alternate phases of muscle-building with contest-preparation work.

PLANNING YOUR CYCLE-TRAINING

For a woman bodybuilder in this country the competitive season begins in February and lasts until September, when the British Championships take place. So, generally speaking, the 'off-season' covers the months from September to February, and the 'season' from February to September. It depends on the individual exactly which contests she decides to enter, depending on her condition. Some girls prefer to enter a qualifying contest early in the season to allow a long break before the British Championships, while others prefer to work-out heavy as long as possible and try to qualify close to the 'Big One'. Whichever way you choose, you will need to plan your whole bodybuilding year in advance from September onwards and allow two peaking phases of approximately two to three months each.

A typical year's plan for a successful national-level competitor might look like this:

September 31st – January 1st	Off-season training for strength and power plus Xmas holiday.
January 1st – April 1st April 2nd	3 months pre-competitive Cycle 1. Qualifying Contest.
Contingency Plan May 5th	1 month's maintenance training until second qualifying contest (if first attempt fails).
If you win first time, then April 3rd–10th	1–2 week lay-off after contest and take a holiday.
April 11th – June 30th	Heavy training and maintenance diet.
July 1st – September 10th	3 months pre-contest Cycle 2.
September 11th	British Championships
Late September	2 week lay-off and holiday.

You can use an outline plan like this to work out exactly how you are going to train and eat for each week of the year.

Personally, I think it is too much of a mental and physical strain to compete more frequently than two or three times in any one season, and much too distracting if you have a job and an otherwise busy life.

The need to stay defined for weeks on end means that gains and progress are virtually impossible and you might easily end the season looking worse than you started.

Holidays are always hard to fit in if you are a competitor, and not many bodybuilders actually enjoy a complete lay-off. Try to fit them into your schedule at a time which will least disrupt your training and progress, and also allow you total relaxation. Don't go for two weeks in Crete just before the British Championships! On the other hand, don't be so manic about training that you never take a break; that is just as bad for you.

TRAINING PROGRESSION

1 The 'Off-Season' Training Cycle

Duration: Allow yourself at least one period of 4 to 6 months annually for off-season training, preferably from September to March.

Aims
1 To increase strength and power.
2 To increase muscle mass as opposed to definition.
3 To improve lagging bodyparts.

Basic Principles of Off-Season Training
1 Train using a split routine, which suits your rest requirements.
2 Use mainly basic exercises (e.g. squat, bench press, deadlift, barbell curl, bentover rows).
3 Use as much weight as you can handle safely and keep pushing yourself to use more.
4 Always work in strict form.
5 Choose barbell or machine exercises.
6 Perform 1 warm-up set, then follow with no more than 6 to 8 sets for large muscle groups, 3 to 4 sets for small muscle groups.
7 Keep reps low (4 to 6 upper body preferably, 10 to 12 lower body).
8 Work to high intensity on all sets.
9 Use forced reps, cheating and other intensifying techniques for a limited number of exercises weekly, taking care not to overtrain.
10 Rest approximately 1 to 2 minutes between sets, longer for large muscle groups if required.
11 Keep your work-outs short – about 1 hour, but put into them everything you've got. This will

mean training no more than 2 or 3 bodyparts per session.

2 The 'Transition' Phase

Allow yourself 1 to 4 weeks to change over from off-season training to a pre-contest régime. Take it gently and don't shock your body by sudden drastic change.

The idea is gradually to intensify your training, at the same time tightening your diet. If you have been following a four-day split, change to five-days now, and continue for about 1 month before further intensification.

3 The Pre-Contest Training Phase

Duration
The time to start this phase will depend on how much weight you have to lose and how you look. Most people allow around 8 to 10 weeks, but if you are already in good shape you could get away with much less.

Aims
Pre-contest training is designed to bring out the maximum degree of defined muscularity, while retaining muscle mass, and good health.

Pre-contest Training Principles
1 Train each muscle group 2 or 3 times weekly on a 5- or 6-day split or double split system.
2 Train faster and harder and virtually non-stop. Faster and more frequent work-outs accelerate the metabolic rate and burn fat.
3 Retain 1 or 2 basic exercises per bodypart, but introduce many more isolation exercises.
4 Continue to use as much weight as you can, but remember that more intense training, coupled with a restricted diet, will increasingly force your weights down to moderate poundages.
5 Switch to dumb-bell and cable exercises.
6 Perform 10 to 12 reps per set.
7 Use up to 15 total sets for small bodyparts, more for large muscles.
8 Quality train, by reducing rest intervals to a maximum 30 seconds between sets.
9 Introduce many more intensification techniques, (e.g. supersets, trisets, pre-exhaustion, etc.).
10 Perform exercises with more mental application and concentration.
11 Use techniques for bringing out detail (e.g. peak contraction, iso-tension).
12 Work-outs should last around 2 hours in this cycle.
13 Employ visualization techniques both in the

gym and in your rest periods, especially at bedtime when your mind is uncluttered.

14 Four weeks prior to the contest introduce 30 minutes of aerobic exercise into your daily schedule (e.g. jogging, swimming, cycling, aerobic dance).

DIETARY PROGRESSION

Off-season Nutrition

During the off-season, the bodybuilder's chief objective is to gain as much quality muscle, with as little fat as possible.

If you gain too much bodyfat during the off-season, you will simply have to work-out and diet very rigorously for many weeks prior to a contest, and in doing so will almost certainly lose muscle size and exhaust yourself. If this cycle continues every year you will never make improvements. Off-season, bodyweight should never exceed 10 percent more than ideal contest weight, and your bodyfat level should not go above 20 percent even then.

The old idea of bulking-up in the off-season and cutting down for a contest is now outmoded, and considered ineffective. In my view, if you are known to be a competitive bodybuilder, it is necessary for the image of the sport at large to look like a bodybuilder all year round, and not just for a few days near a contest. If you look like a Michelin man for the rest of the time, it is not good for your self-image or for bodybuilding. I think this is especially true for anyone who holds an area or national title, since they will frequently be asked for publicity pictures and interviews.

Try to stay within 5 or 7 lbs of contest weight all year round, so that you could be in contest shape within 4 to 6 weeks at any time.

In order to handle heavy weights you will have to allow your bodyweight to rise a little and accept that you cannot be sharply defined all year round. On the other hand, you don't want to look like a thickset power-lifter, so keep your overall calorie intake around 2,000 or 2,500 calories daily. The off-season diet should be basically low-fat, moderate protein, and high complex carbohydrate. It will, over a period of time, with sustained training, alter the ratio of muscle:fat in the body, reducing the fat level and increasing the muscle tissue. It will also supply ample complex carbohydrate to sustain heavy training sessions and provide the essential nutrients in balanced form for tissue repair, growth and stamina.

If you begin to allow junk foods to creep in, review your diet every few weeks and readjust it. Keep a note in your training diary of everything you eat and the way your body reacts. If you find a particular combination of training and diet which provides you with good gains, then stick to it. If you hit a plateau, then experiment with dietary adjustments. Bear in mind your bodytype (endomorph, ectomorph, or mesomorph) and adjust your food intake accordingly.

There is some controversy about the exact proportions of nutrients that a bodybuilder should ingest, but the most popular and successful seems to be 2:1:3 for protein, fat and carbohydrate respectively (or 15 percent fat: 20 to 30 percent protein and the rest complex carbohydrate). This should maintain off-season bodyfat at a reasonably low level and supply all nutritional needs. For weight training, typically, dietary fat demands are low, since the anaerobic nature of the exercise calls mainly on the body's glucose (carbohydrate) supplies. But for this reason, muscle-building protein and energy-giving complex carbohydrates are needed in quantity.

Remember: Short intense training sessions demand a high supply of carbohydrate. Longer sub-maximal work-outs will burn off fat (as in pre-competitive schedules).

Basic off-season low-fat diet

Breakfast
A fresh sliced orange to start.
Any wholegrain cereals: oats, millet, buckwheat, barley, rice flakes with yogurt and fruit.
Herb tea, water, decaffeinated coffee, diluted natural fruit juice.
OR
Fresh fruit, dried fruit and yogurt.
OR
Porridge of oats, millet or rice flakes, soaked dried fruit and ground almonds.
OR
Wholemeal toast plus cottage cheese, grilled toppings, – tomatoes, peppers, mushrooms.
OR
Omelette or scrambled eggs made with 1 egg yolk and 3 egg whites and wholemeal toast.
OR
Skinned grilled chicken and wholemeal toast.
OR
Grilled fish – plaice, cod, kipper and unsalted rice cakes (from good health food stores), flaked smoked haddock with brown rice.

High Energy Breakfast
This meets just about every nutritional need and you certainly won't feel hungry till lunchtime.
1 tbsp. each of millet and buckwheat or rice flakes. Small quantity mixed seeds of pumpkin, sesame, sunflower, linseed, 1 teasp. ground almonds. Moisten with apple or grape juice. Add 2 to 3 pieces of soaked sun-dried fruit (prunes, apricots, apple rings, peaches). 1 sliced banana. 1 spoonful of goat's yogurt or low-fat live yogurt.
Avoid honey or sugared jam. Sugar-free jam is obtainable from health food shops.

Mid-Morning Snack
(If hungry only)
Choose between: fruit, nuts, yogurt, cottage cheese.

Lunchtime
Large mixed salad including sprouted seeds, raw vegetables and parsley. 1 jacket potato. *Toppings:* goat's yogurt or low-fat live yogurt, raisins and nuts, dates, almonds, cottage cheese.   *OR*   Cold grilled plaice, cod, haddock fillets with herbs. 1 slice wholemeal toast or ½ jacket potato.   *OR*   Salmon or tuna fish on wholemeal bread.
Same choice of drinks as breakfast.

Pre-Work-out Snack
½ jacket potato.   *Or* fruit.   *Or* dates.

Dinner
Grilled turkey, chicken or any fish, fresh or tinned (*not in oil*). *Or* cottage cheese, eggs.
Large mixed salad or green leafy vegetable: broccoli, beans or spinach. Brown rice. *Or* pasta. *Or* jacket potato. *Or* wholemeal bread. *Or* root vegetables. Fruit, fresh or stewed.

To Lose Bodyfat

1 Eat this type of food in small portions.
2 Aim to stay a little hungry at the end of a meal.
3 Increase your activities. Walk a lot, jog, swim, cycle, do aerobic dance classes.

Don't weigh yourself, look in the mirror and be critical.

For Muscular Weight Gain

1 Mid-morning and mid-afternoon, add a protein drink, in skimmed milk, with a banana.
2 Eat small meals frequently, each one containing a source of low-fat protein. Don't let yourself get hungry.
3 Rest as much as possible and cut out aerobic exercise.

Here is a sample diet for off-season weight gaining:

High Energy Breakfast
3-egg omelette. Wholemeal toast. Fruit. Supplements. Tea or coffee with milk.

Mid-Morning
Protein shake.

Lunch
Chicken, cheese, egg or tuna salad. Or lean meat. Rice, potatoes or wholemeal bread. Fruit. Milk. Supplements.

Teatime
Protein shake.

Dinner
Chicken. Or cheese. Or eggs. Or fish. Rice, potatoes or wholemeal bread. Vegetables or salad. Fruit. Supplements.

Supper
Protein shake. Or chicken. Or tuna. Or egg. Or lean meat sandwich.

Remember:

If you end a meal hungry – you're losing.
If you end a meal satisfied – you're stable.
If you end a meal full – you're gaining.

GETTING RIPPED

Every competitor has their own secret way of getting 'ripped' or 'cut-up'. The general idea is to reduce your bodyfat levels as low as possible, in order to show your developed muscles clearly, together with the lines which divide and separate them. It is this 'definition' which every competitor seeks to achieve. If you have too much bodyfat, you will look 'smooth', and all your training will be for nothing.

Do be warned that your appearance whilst 'ripped' will not conform to the generally accepted standard of feminine beauty. You will probably lose your bust, and have prominent veins in your arms. Your face may look drawn. If you want muscular definition for a contest, then these are factors to consider. It might be worth warning the man in your life or your mother what to expect! It will only be for a short time, and you will soon recover your more rounded contours.

Don't *ever* be tempted to try to stay 'ripped' all the time. Not only does it look rather unattractive for everyday purposes, but it would also be extremely unhealthy to maintain such low bodyfat. It is very dangerous to lose sight of your own image in the mirror and to think that extreme definition is desirable. Aim for healthy muscular shape, *never* emaciation.

As I explained earlier, it is very difficult to cheat the body into losing bodyfat without losing muscle at the same time, so over the years bodybuilders have experimented with all manner of diets and training régimes to try to find the right formula and be in peak condition on the day of the contest. The aim is precise – you must look your ultimate on one day only and better than everyone else on stage. If you miss that target by 24 hours either way, you will be beaten. Some really top-class international professionals never quite make it because they cannot discover how to 'peak' on schedule. You will only learn how to do it by experience, since only you can judge exactly the way your own body will react. The advice in this section therefore is only that – advice. It may work for you or it may not, but in principle it should be effective for most people.

Bodybuilders are the only athletes who have to make their maximum training effort on the least amount of food, so it is essential that what you eat is high quality, and provides you with enough energy to train.

If you have followed a sensible diet in the off-season, you should not have a major weight loss problem prior to competition. I am assuming that up to this point you have been training consistently with heavy weights, and following a sensible diet to maintain your strength. During the off-season period you will probably have sacrificed your definition somewhat, and allowed your bodyweight to rise in order to handle heavy weights. But around 12 weeks from a contest your approach will need to change.

A 1,000-calorie intake, in a balanced combination, will enable you to continue training hard. If you eat nothing but tuna, chicken and grapefruit for three months or follow some other cranky diet, you may lose weight, but you will also create a chronic dietary imbalance in your body, together with a vitamin and mineral deficiency. You will have no energy to train, a drawn, listless appearance (which will be marked down by the judges), an irritable temper, and after the show you will probably binge and feel right out of sorts. A sensible reduction of 500 calories daily from your normal diet over a period of time should ensure a weight loss of 1 kilo (approximately 2 lbs) per week, provided it is combined with vigorous exercise. Most women will lose weight using this approach, but you must continue to take in enough protein and carbohydrate to build and retain muscle size.

Building muscle should continue until the last minute, so the diet needs to take this into account. You should not need to vary the recommended off-season ratio of 2:1:3 – protein:fat:carbohydrate (unless you use the glycogen loading technique in the immediate pre-contest period (see p. 146).

If you take a long period to lose your fat this way, it will cause you the least possible discomfort and minimize muscle loss. Keep checking on your progress in the mirror. If you lose weight too quickly and begin to look scrawny, then step up your calories for a few days.

One point to remember is that it is diet which will make your waist and abdominal muscles look sensational. There is no need to kill yourself doing thousands of sit-ups, twists and leg raises. If you have built up your abs. with weights in the off-season, they will automatically become defined as you lose bodyfat. While watching your calorie intake, eat small quantities of food frequently through the day. This will shrink your stomach and improve abdominal definition by keeping it flat.

For a novice competitor, there is no point in getting so 'ripped' that your bones stick through, making you look like a famine victim. At this stage you will not have sufficient muscle bulk to enable you to look shapely if you are over-thin. Far better to be less enthusiastic about definition and maintain any muscle size you have built. The judges will not expect beginners to have zero bodyfat in any case.

Further up the competitive ladder, women will have much more muscularity after training for a period of several years and will gradually have replaced fat with muscle. At their level, with knowledge and experience, it is possible to achieve maximum definition and muscularity at the same time and look both lean and big. Remember, bodybuilders should not have visible bones. When you are ripped, you want to show your muscles, not your skeleton.

If you follow these principles, in combination with a pre-competitive training programme which includes aerobic exercise, you will soon be 'ripped to shreds'!

First of all, work out how much fat you need to lose to achieve your optimum appearance. Get some expert advice on this. Ideally have it accurately assessed. Reckon on losing 1 lb per week, then count backwards from your selected contest to see how soon you should begin. Let us assume you are 10 lbs over contest weight, so therefore begin to tighten your diet 10 weeks in advance. Never try to lose more than 1 or 2 lbs maximum per week. If you try to lose weight any faster than this, you will only lose water, and worse, muscle tissue. If you wish to maintain muscle bulk and lose fat, then the process must be very slow indeed. Remember that the ratio of fat:muscle loss encountered on an average diet is 1 lb muscle:2 lbs fat.

It is very important to change from an off-season to a pre-competitive diet very gradually. It is far too much of a shock for the system to launch straight into an entirely different régime. The body may even start to store fat in reaction. There should be a gradual transitional phase, building up to a peak. The same goes for the reverse transition from a pre-competitive to an off-season régime – take it easy. You should never need to diet drastically if you begin in good time. If you do leave it too late and lose weight too fast, you will not allow your skin a chance to tighten up. You will end up with loose hanging skinfolds and look awful.

All you need to do is ensure that your energy output is lower than your intake, nothing more drastic than that. Make sure too that as your diet becomes more restricted, you increase your supplementation.

The Pre-Contest Diet

The pre-contest diet is generally regarded as the worst part of bodybuilding. It sorts out the committed from the just interested, and almost has the status of a ritual, or initiation rite. There are plenty of women, and men too, who have tried it once and made it such an ordeal that they are put off ever competing again. It really need not be as bad as all that.

Personally I'd prefer to work-out in the gym six times as hard rather than diet but, in the long run, the battle is at the dinner table not on the pec. dec. machine, if you want to look magnificent.

Methods of Pre-Competitive Dieting

1 Low Carbohydrate

Bodybuilders are about equally divided in favour of low-carbohydrate or low-fat dieting methods, although women bodybuilders tend to favour the latter. Low-fat dieting is the newer method, and it is certainly less uncomfortable.

The advantages of low-carbohydrate dieting are:

i. You will see initial results fast, because as carbohydrates are withdrawn, you lose the considerable quantities of water that they retain in the body. But after this, progress tends to slow down considerably.

ii. You can eat fats on a low-carbohydrate diet, since they cannot be converted to fat without carbohydrates being present. Eating fats tends to kill the appetite, because they are digested slowly and release energy slowly into the bloodstream, so preventing blood-sugar levels plummeting.

If you want to try a low-carbohydrate diet, obtain a chart giving the carbohydrate content of foods. But be sensible and don't attempt a nil-carb. diet. Cut back carbohydrates gradually and do not go below 30 grams per day.

On a low-carb. diet fresh fruit and vegetables will be very limited, and you could become badly deficient in vital nutrients, so it is doubly necessary to boost your vitamin/mineral supplement well above normal level.

Here is a typical day's eating on a low-carb. diet:

Breakfast
¼ melon Eggs, meat, fish Coffee with cream Double supplements
Lunch
Cheese or meat Small salad with oil/vinegar dressing Double supplements
Teatime
Eggs, cheese, meat Tea with milk
Dinner
Roast meat, cold meat *Or* eggs *Or* cheese Small salad Double supplements

There are a few low-carb. fruits you can eat, such as melons and strawberries.

Watch out for sodium in the usual way, but be especially careful in the final 2 weeks before the contest.

The drawbacks of low-carbohydrate dieting:

i.   It lowers the blood-sugar level drastically. This starves your brain of the only fuel it can use, and you cannot concentrate and feel sleepy all the time.

ii. You become irritable, nervous, highly emotional, bad tempered and, if you are foolish enough to try a nil-carb. diet, practically suicidal. This is bad for you, but even worse for your family and colleagues!

iii. Because your energy level is so low, you can't get a decent work-out. Your weights have to come down and you have no stamina.

iv. In the absence of carbohydrate, the body turns to protein for fuel. This is a lengthy conversion process using even more energy which you can't spare. The protein used will derive from the muscles, so you lose size.

143

v. The body is so starved of carbohydrate that after the contest is over you will have to endure an irresistible carbohydrate-bloat, and this will make you feel bad and look worse. You could easily blow out 14 lbs in a week.

2 Calorie Counting

Some bodybuilders still swear by this method, which involves meticulously weighing every scrap of food you eat and looking up its calorific value in a calorie counter. The advantage is that you can eat anything you like, as long as you stop at 1,000 calories, or whatever limit you set.

Personally, I think you need a willpower of steel to survive this method and I really admire anyone who can do it. I certainly cannot! There are few people who can stop after eating 1 oz of chocolate cake or three chips. I don't recommend this technique, but if you wish to try it, women's magazines are full of variations on this old-fashioned theme. However, as a bodybuilder, *remember* to watch your sodium intake all the time and take your supplements.

3 Low-Fat Dieting

This is the method I favour, and so do most other women bodybuilders because it is painless, and it works.

It is a dietary régime which can and should be followed all year round to keep bodyfat levels permanently low. It is a very healthy eating pattern and makes you feel good. It does not induce hunger pangs or cravings. (The basic principles of this type of diet have already been explained in more detail on p. 139.)

A low-fat diet creates a shortfall in the number of calories you burn-up each day. Once the deficit is around 500 calories daily, you will lose 1 lb of bodyfat each week. One gram of fat produces 9 calories, 1 gram of protein or carbohydrate only 4 calories, so by cutting out fats you can create a deficit much faster and more effectively. If you obtain a food chart giving fat contents of all food, you can select the foods with the lowest fat content on a scientific basis. You will not create a nutritional imbalance in your body following this diet, so vitamin supplements are not as vital in megadoses. The only disadvantage of a long-term low-fat diet is that your skin may become a little dry. If so, use body oil after you bathe. This type of diet allows your muscles to continue their growth and maintain their size. A low-fat, moderate protein, high-carb. diet is your best and most healthy bet. Here is a suggested day's menu, which can be followed for two months, stopping about four weeks short of a contest.

Low-fat eating plan for two months prior to a contest (until final four weeks):

Breakfast
On getting up: 1 tbspn. cider vinegar in water. 1 tbspn. cereal (oats, millet, rice flakes), grated apple or sliced orange or pear. 1 oz mixed seeds (sunflower, pumpkin, linseed or sesame). A little apple juice to moisten. 1 tbspn. low-fat yogurt. *OR* Fruit and low-fat yogurt. *OR* Chicken and 1 slice wholemeal toast. *OR* Fish (haddock, cod, plaice). 2 salt-free rice crackers. ½ orange. Herb tea and supplements.

Snack
1 piece fruit.

Lunch
Salad (with cider vinegar and lemon wedges). Chicken or fish. Herb tea and supplements. *OR* Yogurt and fruit (apple, pear, strawberries, raspberries, peach). Herb tea and supplements. *OR* Cottage cheese and fruit. Herb tea and supplements.

Snack
1 piece fruit.

Dinner
Salad or green leafy vegetables. Turkey, chicken, fish, cottage cheese. Water with lemon. Supplements.

Four Weeks Before a Contest

1 Follow the same general principles, but count your calories too.
2 Eliminate any junk food which may have crept into your daily intake, cut out all sugar and alcohol.
3 Phase out grain products which retain water, and cut out protein drinks.
4 Eliminate eggs, red meat and anything other than low-fat dairy products.
5 Remove root vegetables and substitute salad and green leafy vegetables. Cut out fruit juices and drink herb teas, black coffee, spring water or fresh lemon juice.
6 Take a tablespoonful of cider vinegar in water daily.

The final two weeks before a contest are critical, and can make or break your chances of winning. This is where you will have to resign yourself to some suffering.

Limit your diet to chicken or turkey breast, white fish, plain low-fat yogurt, egg whites, tuna, green salads, jacket potatoes, a little brown rice and low-calorie fruits such as melon, strawberries, apples, oranges.

My Pre-Contest Diet

In preparing for about ten contests during the past three seasons, I have evolved my own personal pre-contest diet. I cannot stress enough that this is what works for *me*, and that everyone is different.

I start to cut back gradually on my general food intake about 12 weeks in advance of a contest, and begin my serious diet about 6 weeks in advance, depending on the amount of bodyfat I have to lose.

Normally, I begin to train on a 3 days on, 1 day off cycle at the same time, and my diet follows the same pattern.

TRAINING DAYS

8.30 a.m.   Breakfast

1 sliced fresh orange.
4–6 oz portion of plain grilled fresh fish (plaice, cod or haddock).
Black coffee.
Supplements.

1.30 p.m.   Lunch

1 small carton cottage cheese with pineapple
OR
4 oz fresh prawns
with salad of lettuce, tomato, cucumber, parsley and sliced lemon.
Black tea or coffee.
Supplements.

4.00 p.m.

(2 hours prior to work-out)
1 apple or pear or strawberries.

9.30 p.m.   Dinner

12 oz grilled fish (cod, haddock, skate, halibut, plaice) with lemon juice and herbs
OR
6 oz grilled turkey breast.
A large salad consisting of as many of the following as possible: lettuce, watercress, cress, tomato, cucumber, fennel, raw cauliflower, broccoli, spinach, carrots, fresh parsley or mint, white cabbage, green pepper, onions, radishes, etc.
Dressing of lemon or cider vinegar (if any at all)
AND/OR
Whole French beans or broccoli or spinach.
Fresh fruit, either apple, pear, peach, strawberries, melon or apricots.
Black coffee.
Supplements.

The cottage cheese is cut out in the last two weeks as it contains salt. Also, as I am allergic to chicken, tuna, milk, eggs, bread and soya, I cannot include any of these.

I follow this plan for 3 days. As it is low in carbohydrates I start to feel rather weak and listless, so on Day 4 I add a jacket potato, or large plate of brown rice. This has the advantage of preventing constipation as well as replenishing my glycogen stores during my rest day. The following day I retain some water as a result and lose a little definition, but this disappears in 24 hours. Because of the consequent boost in my energy level, I do my heaviest leg work-out on the next day.

Occasionally I allow myself one treat – dry white wine.

In the final two weeks prior to competition I cut out these extra complex carbohydrates until the final day before the contest, when I eat no protein at all, only complex carbohydrates in small quantities throughout the day in order to 'carb.-up'.

I stick to exactly the same food every day. This is incredibly boring and unbalanced, but if I vary it, I start to cheat. As long as I keep taking plenty of supplements, I feel really healthy and my skin definitely improves.

Pre-Contest Diet Tips

1 Watch out all the time for sodium, which will cause water retention and blur your hard-earned definition. Be really neurotic close to a contest. Don't have cottage cheese, sea fish or celery, which are all high in sodium. Look up everything you intend to eat in *The Salt Counter*.
2 Black coffee will help to burn extra fat and get you through your final gruelling aerobic work-outs.
3 For the final week, cut out all other liquids except distilled water (the kind you can buy at the chemist for use in steam irons and which is sold in gallon containers). Use this for your coffee, if you can't do without it!
4 Keep eating small snacks throughout the day to keep your stomach flat, your blood-sugar level up and your metabolism burning.
5 Keep eating complex carbohydrates in combination with protein to protect your muscle bulk.
6 The final pre-contest diet is frankly unbalanced, unhealthy and deficient. It does not contain all the essential nutrients and would be impossible to maintain for any length of time. You should supplement your food intake with up to double your normal vitamin/mineral intake at this time.

As your stomach rumbles in bed at night, concentrate your thoughts (positively) on that winner's trophy!

Glycogen-loading and 'Carbing-Up'

Some bodybuilders now employ a technique developed by marathon runners to enhance the appearance of their muscles for a contest.

Seven days before a contest, the athlete performs a long aerobic work-out to exhaustion point. This burns up all the 'glycogen' stores in the muscles and the liver, the body's energy reserve tank. For the next 3 days, carbohydrates are reduced to an absolute minimum and protein and fat alone are eaten. Then for the final 4 days the switch is made to a high carbohydrate, low protein and fat diet, with an almost exclusively carbohydrate intake in the immediate 24 hours before the contest as protein is no longer needed for muscle growth at this stage. The net result is that the body over-reacts, refilling its glycogen stores to a level up to three times as high as usual. It is most important to rest completely while this process is taking place, and not to take any further strenuous exercise for 24 to 48 hours. For marathon runners the effect is to give them an energy boost at the critical phase of the race, so delaying the inevitable onset of fatigue after two hours of all-out effort. For bodybuilders, however, the surplus glycogen attracts more water back into the muscles, causing them to increase in bulk. This is perfectly timed for contest day. But you must be very careful when employing this technique not to overdo the 'carbing-up' or you may begin to retain water all over and smooth out. You must therefore keep counting your calories and eat only small meals, or you will rapidly gain weight and lose your contest definition. There is a very fine line between peak condition and going over the edge. Anyone wanting to experiment with this technique should have a dry run when it doesn't really matter how you look.

Diuretics and Dehydration

The use of natural diuretics before competition is unnecessary if you have meticulously watched your sodium intake. Your water retention should be just about nil. If you take diuretics in this condition, they will take water from the muscles and you will smooth out, wrecking weeks of hard-won definition overnight. I know, because I've done it!

Strong diuretic drugs should *never* be taken. They are downright dangerous, and can even kill you. It doesn't look good if you faint on stage from low blood pressure, due to reduced blood volume. You will also be completely incapable of 'pumping up' in this condition. If you must take something, take extra Vitamin C, drink parsley tea, or use Boldo tablets with discretion.

Pre-Contest Aerobics

For competitive bodybuilders, it is important to fit into your pre-competition cycle at least half an hour's aerobic activity daily in addition to your normal work-out. This will increase general fitness and stamina, as well as helping you gain maximum definition by raising the metabolic rate and burning off the fat. Try to do the aerobics either at least 3 hours before your weight work-out or after it, otherwise you will have little energy left for the gym.

A very good form of pre-contest aerobic exercise is *circuit weight-training*. This is the aerobic form of weight-training which simultaneously develops general fitness, cardiovascular condition and muscular endurance by exercising continuously for over ten minutes. It is useful for those seeking a good general conditioning programme for fitness, endurance and improved strength; those wishing to lose weight; competitive bodybuilders in a pre-contest phase, and athletes needing local muscular endurance for their sport (e.g. cyclists, rowers, skiers).

A typical circuit would consist of about 10 or 15 exercises, covering all the major muscle groups and set out in a pre-determined sequence around a large room. A combination of apparatus and free-standing exercises is performed. Each piece of apparatus is pre-set with a fairly light weight and each exercise 'station' marked with an indication of how many times a specific exercise should be performed.

Normally, a group of people trains together around a circuit of different exercises. Each starts at a different place in the room, repeats the specific exercise at that point a predetermined number of times (or reps) and then proceeds to the next station. The first circuit might include 20 reps of each exercise. Rest intervals are minimal. One or two more circuits can be performed. The whole session should be against the clock. As participants get fitter, and the cardiovascular effort required decreases, the weights used are increased to make the circuit harder. The general idea is to keep on working for a long period of time, without stopping. The overall effect, if continued regularly, is improved fitness, endurance and weight loss. This type of weight-training is ideal for toning, conditioning and weight loss. Competitive bodybuilders use circuit training prior to a contest to bring out definition and use it as an intensive form of quality training.

Maintenance Training Diet Between Contests

If you intend to enter several contests in one season, it is necessary to maintain your condition from one to the next. Remember you cannot expect to stay razor sharp all the time, and the pre-competitive diet is impossible to sustain. You will have to allow for a few pounds to return between contests. Put back into your diet the foods you took out of it in reverse order, but be careful not to overdo it. Continue your régime of chicken, fish, salad, green vegetables, low-calorie fruit, jacket potatoes and a little brown rice or pasta. Watch out for sodium as usual. Stay away from your weaknesses for the moment! Allow yourself 2 or 3 weeks before your next contest to tighten your diet and re-sharpen your definition.

Once the season is over, you can relax and revert to your off-season plan, and higher calorie intake, but take it easily and only gradually re-introduce the foods you eliminated. If you suddenly revert, you will look and feel bloated, retain excessive water and feel miserable. If you pile in the carbs after eating very little for weeks, you will feel really poisoned since your system cannot produce enough insulin to cope with the surfeit of blood sugar. Most competitors have experienced a rapidly beating heart after a post-contest carbohydrate binge, and it is not pleasant.

Chapter Nine

COMPETITIONS

Very few women who take up weight-training have any intention of competing. If someone had told me when I began that two years later I would be in the British Bodybuilding Championships, I would have been amazed.

There comes a point when you begin to see results from all your hard training, and at first, somewhat secretively, you flex your biceps in front of the bedroom mirror. Then you are tempted to compare your development with other women at a similar stage of training. If you are lucky enough to belong to a gym where women bodybuilders train and compete regularly, then the excitement of preparing for a contest is infectious and will inevitably rub off on you.

I think the main reason why women are initially so diffident about competing is that we are conditioned not to push ourselves forward or to be conspicuously confident about our physical appearance. This is considered vain and egocentric and we are anxious not to put ourselves in a position where we may be ridiculed. These are ingrained mental attitudes which women have to overcome, and it is not easy to do so. Once they are overcome and the woman accepts her new appearance with relaxed confidence, then she is ready to face a panel of judges and an audience.

It is always a very nerve-racking experience to compete for the first time. Most athletes can make their mistakes at small regional meetings, well away from their local crowd of friends, but women bodybuilders have no choice but to make their début on stage in a bikini in front of a large, predominantly male audience. That is enough to paralyse even the most confident woman.

However, bodybuilding audiences are invariably sympathetic. Most of them are fellow bodybuilders, friends from the gym or family who have suffered with you, through every agonizing day of pre-contest diet and training. They are all there to cheer you and support you, not to criticize. A bodybuilding audience can be guaranteed to cheer most loudly for competitors with the least spectacular physiques, who have obviously worked hard anyway, and had the courage to get up on stage and perform. The most strident criticisms are always from those people who know they have neither the physique nor the nerve to do the same.

Once you decide to compete, you step beyond the point where your weight-training is a recreation to tone up your body, and you enter the realms of bodybuilding as a competitive sport. If you really want to succeed you have to make a commitment to a whole new way of life, for to be a competitor is a serious business. The standard of women's bodybuilding competition in this country has risen remarkably since I started, as more and more girls have become involved and no doubt will continue to do so. Many of these started bodybuilding when they had already been involved in, or grown tired of, other competitive sports such as power-lifting, gymnastics, skating, swimming, martial arts and so on and they already had the advantage of muscularity and flexibility. It is therefore important to bear in mind that it takes time to develop a physique good enough to win at regional or national level. If you are starting from scratch, that will mean at least 2 to 5 years of regular hard training. Of course, much depends on the physique you start with. If you have good potential – a shapely physique with good natural proportions, a mesomorphic body type, and the right genetics to build muscle easily – then you will make rapid progress. Anyone who is initially very overweight or underweight will take correspondingly longer to develop. However, good bodybuilders have been produced from the most unpromising material, and often those who have the least natural potential and most problems to overcome work hardest and beat the 'natural' stars.

Remember that it takes time and experience. Do not give up because you do not win your first contest.

If you keep training steadily, you will eventually improve and your day will come, while others give up and fall by the wayside. All that matters is that on the day of the contest you know that you have put 110 percent effort into your training, your diet and your posing routine, and are standing on stage in the best condition of your life, whether it is your first novice contest or 'Miss Olympia'. Each time you compete, strive to improve on your last appearance. If you have not improved, don't compete. The battle is never really with the other competitors, but with yourself, and the way you looked three months, six months or a year previously. Stick to it, be patient, and you will come out top!

HOW CONTESTS ARE ORGANIZED

The parent organization for world bodybuilding is the International Federation of Bodybuilders, founded in 1946 by Ben and Joe Weider. The IFBB organizes international amateur and professional contests for men and women. More than one hundred countries have their own branches of the Federation, which are affiliated to the IFBB. In this country it is the English Federation of Bodybuilders.

Bodybuilding is a recognized competitive sport, and the EFBB is a member of the Central Council for Physical Recreation, as well as being affiliated to the general Association of International Sports Federations and the International Council of Sports and Physical Education. In Britain there is no separate Federation as yet for women alone, as there is in the USA, where the amateur women's sport is organized by the AFWB (American Federation of Women Bodybuilders).

Although bodybuilding is not yet included in the Olympic Games, it is now part of the World Games – a major international competition for both men and women in minor sports which are not yet Olympic events. It is possible that bodybuilding could one day become an Olympic sport, if the Olympic Games themselves can survive in their present form. The main obstacle facing bodybuilding is the thorny problem of drug-testing, and until the sport can overcome this well-known abuse, it will remain an outsider.

In this country, the EFBB holds a series of regional contests throughout the spring and early summer, starting in February or March. The weight-class winners of the area shows qualify for the British Championships, which are held in the autumn. Anyone who wins an area contest is automatically excluded from competing in further qualifying events in order to give other competitors a chance. If a competitor fails to win in her own area, then she may compete in other areas as many times

as it may take her to qualify. A competitor who is consistently placed high throughout the season, but who fails to win outright, may also be invited to the British Championships. Now that so many girls are training hard and competing, the numbers appearing at area shows are increasing rapidly, and a line-up might attract ten to fifteen girls of good standard. It is therefore a real mark of success to be invited to the British finals, for every girl on stage will already be an area champion and have beaten many other competitors just to qualify.

The winners of the two weight classes in the British Championships go forward to the team selection for the European Championships the following spring. They will also probably be given the chance to compete in at least one international match during the year, perhaps with Holland or Belgium, and so qualify for the honour of wearing the 'England' insignia on their tracksuits. Some winners of big area shows may also be selected to take part in international contests.

The winners of the European Championships, usually held in April or May, may be invited to enter the ultimate women's contest, 'Miss Olympia' – which is held in the USA in the autumn. One British competitor, Carolyn Cheshire, our only professional woman bodybuilder, has entered the 'Miss Olympia' contest. She has competed in every one since the first held in 1980, and was placed seventh in 1983. Maybe one day we shall see a British 'Miss Olympia'.

All contests staged by the EFBB in this country are amateur. However, in the last three years Britain has started to host some major international shows organized by the IFBB. These include the European Championships, 'Mr Olympia', Women's World Championships, Men's Professional Grand Prix Finals and in 1985 the World Games at Wembley in which bodybuilding for women is prominently featured.

London has again become a world centre for top-class bodybuilding after a gap of many years, and much of the impetus for this renaissance has been the publicity given to the rise of women's bodybuilding and its inclusion as a separate and equally important event in most major contests.

In the USA, the AFWB organize contests on a State to State basis, and the winners go forward to the amateur Miss America competition. Some State contests are open to international competitors who can enter as long as they are AFWB members and can fulfil a short residential requirement (30 days).

As women's bodybuilding in the USA is much more developed than in Britain, there are professional contests as well, where prize money is offered, and a Grand Prix Circuit is developing for the top professional competitors. This is also now being extended to include European countries as well.

To rank as a professional does not necessarily mean that you work in bodybuilding full-time, although a few top competitors do so. It merely means that you have accepted prize money and have thereby excluded yourself from competing in amateur contests in the future. For the really successful few, TV and promotional work, marketing of personalized products, TV commercials and even film roles can all provide lucrative careers, but for the majority this is only a heady dream. No wonder that with such glittering prizes on offer, some competitors are tempted to cheat by taking the dangerous short-cut provided by drugs, and choosing success and money above health and fitness.

Needless to say, the competitive sport of women's bodybuilding has absolutely no connection with beauty competitions. Top women competitors are highly trained athletes, and also unquestionably the most beautiful women in the world!

HOW AND WHEN TO ENTER A CONTEST

Once you have decided that you would like to enter a contest, you should join the EFBB. You must be a member of the Federation on the day of the show. It is usually possible to join at the show itself, if you have failed to do so in advance.

Be very critical of your condition before you make your final decision about competing, and get an opinion from someone who has experience of contests – a former competitor, a judge or experienced trainer. Because the standard is now so high, it is inadvisable to compete before you are really ready. You will only be disheartened, and may not bother again. Most girls, with regular hard training and a good diet, should be ready to compete within 18 months to 2 years, although there will obviously be some talented exceptions.

The area contests are all advertised well in advance in the EFBB's official magazine, so buy a copy and look at the list for the coming season. You may decide you are ready for an area championship, but most beginners now choose to start their competitive careers at the annual all-novices show held in December in London, 'Stars of Tomorrow'. This contest has certainly earned its title, since many winners have gone on to become British Champions.

It is a bad mistake to go in for several shows in your first season. Many girls do so from an excess of enthusiasm and live to regret it. The business of preparing for a contest is an enormous physical and mental strain, and when you are continually dieting and 'cutting-up', you cannot make muscular gains as well. As a result, you could very well end the season in much worse shape than you began it. So be less ambitious and limit yourself to one or two shows at most.

It would be foolhardy to enter a show without having first attended several as a spectator. Make a point of choosing the bigger contests where you will see a good line-up of quality competitors on stage, and try to attend the British Championships. You will then be able to see exactly what happens on stage during the pre-judging and the evening show. You will be able to assess the standard to which you aspire and see some of the opposition in action. You will get some idea about how to approach your posing routine and which music is most effective from the audience point of view. Most of all, the atmosphere of the occasion will rub off on you, and by the end of the evening you will be very sorry that you are only in the audience and not up on the stage holding a trophy!

Your next step is to write to the organizer of the contest you have selected to request an application form to compete in his show. The addresses can all be found in the official EFBB Magazine *Bodybuilding Monthly*. The British Championships, the team selection for the European Championships and most of the internationals are by invitation only. Make your application in good time. You will not be able to make a final decision about the weight class you are in until quite soon before the contest if you are on the border-line. There are two weight classes in Britain, lightweight (under 52k), and middleweight (over 52k). In the USA there is also a heavyweight class, and sometimes a separate class for competitors over 35 years of age.

I have already discussed the basic methods of training and dieting used by competitive bodybuilders, so this section will concentrate on all the other aspects of pre-contest preparation during the final weeks.

THE ART OF POSING

Posing is the method by which bodybuilders display their developed physiques at a contest.

Once your pre-contest training routine and diet are under control, you can begin to think about posing. This is an intimidating prospect for most novices and for many more advanced competitors too. Some girls are lucky enough to be naturally graceful, flexible, and have a sense of rhythm. If you lack any or all of these attributes, you will have to work hard to overcome these disadvantages.

The standard of posing at national and

Opposite and overleaf, two of my favourite competition poses

international competitions level these days is quite staggering. Women bodybuilders have advanced posing far beyond the once rudimentary men's posing and turned it into an interpretative art-form. In turn, women's posing has caused the men to think again, and the standard has risen all round. It is hard to imagine that the cleverly choreographed women's routines, combining intricate muscle poses, dance movements, gymnastics and rhythm can ever have been regarded as too masculine and powerful. No one who has ever watched the feline grace of a top competitor in action could question the beauty and sensuality of female muscle.

a. *Choice of Music*

If you have been to a few contests, you will know that a clever choice of music can go a long way towards success. If you can find something which whips up audience enthusiasm and participation, you are halfway there. You will realize that it is no good posing to 'Swan Lake' if the last competitor used 'Rocky III' or 'War of the Worlds', because it will be an anti-climax, and the audience will be bored and not support you.

Bear in mind the physique and the personality that you wish to project and choose music which enhances both aspects of yourself. Are you slim and elegant and beautifully proportioned, or chunky, muscular and full of bounce?

Your choice of music should have interesting highspots where you can hit your poses, a reasonably slow beat that allows you to hold poses for a few seconds and then progress without haste to a definite climax. Most disco music is too fast for posing. It is always better to select an orchestral rather than a vocal track, which can be distracting. The rules state that the free posing routine must last no longer than 1½ minutes, so edit and pre-record your music to conform. If you go on longer, you will simply be cut off in the middle and sent off stage.

Record your music on two separate cassettes. Mark one clearly 'Pre-Judging', and one 'Evening Show'. Add your name and contest number to each cassette on the day of the show. Make sure each cassette is wound back to the start prior to the contest and give clear instructions to the disc jockey about your requirements.

b. *Choice of Poses*

You have 1½ minutes to fill, so you will have time for about 15 poses, plus linking passages, each pose being held for about 4 seconds. Your first step is to go through some old back copies of muscle

magazines, looking at photographs taken at major women's contests.

Mark with a cross the poses which appeal to you most. Remember to consider your bodytype and select poses which are being demonstrated by someone vaguely similar to yourself physically. Remember too that many top competitors are extremely flexible, which you may not be as yet, so avoid really contorted poses, and also any which require a delicate balancing act. You will be nervous on stage and will almost certainly wobble or lose control if you attempt anything too complicated, and this looks bad. Having short-listed your chosen poses, try them out yourself in front of a mirror, wearing a bikini. At first, you should concentrate only on copying the shape of each pose. Watch yourself in the mirror and try the pose from several different angles. Sometimes a twist of the waist or slight lean backwards can make all the difference.

Really look at yourself critically. The free posing round allows you to show off your good points, and you are under no obligation to show your bad ones, so underplay or disguise them. If you have weak abs. or legs, do not include any poses which emphasize them. Stick to your back or arms which may be good, and attract attention to them instead by means of a clever choice of poses.

Once you can perform an individual pose from memory, you can start to work out the linking movements.

c. *Flexibility*

When you first start to move around and work out your posing routine, you may well suddenly realize just how stiff you are, so it is a very good idea to include some stretching and flexibility exercises in your daily routine. If you have time try to fit in an ordinary keep-fit class every day or two, as this will help. If not, the warm-up stretches described earlier in this book will help.

d. *Choreography*

The judges will want to see your physique from every side, so base your routine on a series of movements which take you from front to side to back to side to front, or some similar sequence. You will probably have to perform on a podium of a limited size, so mark a 6 ft × 4 ft oblong on your practice floor and work inside it.

You can begin to work out your routine by using the compulsory poses in sequence, then gradually adapt and personalize them, adding your own inventive ideas. Avoid using too many floor poses. It does not look very elegant to roll around on the dirty stage, covered in oil and fluff, and the judges and audience can easily lose sight of you as they will be sitting below your level.

Start with a really strong pose to capture the audience's attention, maybe your best one – perhaps with your back to the audience, swing around, flex hard and hold it, then go into your routine. If you adopt a circular routine, it is easier to remember the sequence when you are nervous. Try not to repeat poses for the same bodypart. Remember always to keep your stomach tucked right in and never allow it to relax. The strong flexed poses need to be linked by graceful arm movements and attention to line.

It is advisable at this stage, once you have some idea of your basic routine, to seek advice from a dancer or gymnast or movement teacher about the finer details.

Start to practise away from the mirror as well as in front of it, and go through your routine in different locations from many different angles, so you are not put off by unfamiliar surroundings when you get on stage.

Be aware of your hand movements – the audience's eyes will follow them. Remember to keep your head up, your shoulders relaxed, and your feet neatly placed. An ugly flexed foot can wreck the appearance of an entire pose. Remember to smile or at least to look as if you are enjoying yourself but don't overdo it. A look of concentration is best. After

all, nobody expects other female athletes to perform with a sickly grin.

Don't allow your dance instructor to 'water down' your posing if you want to power pose. This is not a dance, but a bodybuilding routine. Don't include any movements reminiscent of a stripper, since the judges could penalize you for it and, in any case, it is bad for the image of women's bodybuilding. Avoid all awkward poses, especially the 'most muscular' or 'crab' pose, which is totally unsuitable for women, and any ungainly outstretched leg positions.

e. *Flexing*

The free-posing routine is much more than a series of nicely choreographed dance movements. This is the sport of bodybuilding, and it is muscles that the judges want to see. Learning how to find your muscles and flex and hold them in a pose is an art in itself. It is a very exhausting business, so during rehearsals you will not be able to contract your muscles all the time. When you get to the last week or two prior to a contest, however, it is a help to do so, since repeated flexing burns the calories and helps to define the muscles ('isotension').

When you assume a pose, always start from the floor upwards, position and flex your legs first, then your arms, then suck in your mid-section and

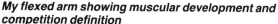
My flexed arm showing muscular development and competition definition

tighten the muscles or twist. Remember to emphasize the muscles you wish to display in that particular pose, but do not completely neglect other areas. A sure sign of a beginner is that their legs are forgotten altogether. Be graceful, feminine and flowing in every move you make on stage, and never relax for an instant, because the judges' eyes will always be watching you.

f. Entrance and Exit

Practise your entrance and exit. Don't just slump on stage and hang around waiting for the music to start. Make sure your posture is immaculate. Use the music all the way from the wings to get you on to the rostrum. You might include a pose halfway across the stage, or run on with enthusiasm and energy, or even walk on slowly in the aristocratic style of a ballet dancer. Choose whichever way suits you, and then get off stage just as gracefully. Nothing looks worse than a hurried, self-conscious embarrassed exit, falling over your feet. Always strive to appear confident, in control, proud and as charismatic as possible. Be sure not to jump off the posing rostrum with your back to the judges. This will make every scrap of fat on your thighs and backside wobble like a blancmange – not a very imposing exit.

Once you have your routine organized, and your poses set, then rehearse and rehearse until you know them back to front, and can add that extra dimension of interpretation which will make the routine really special.

Always keep it short and snappy and leave the audience wanting more, not less. The longer you stay on stage, the more faults the judge will spot.

g. Posing Costume

EFBB contest rules require the costume to be a bikini of one colour, without any ornamentation or glitter. It may not be metallic. Other than that, you can choose any shape or size, provided that it is decent. The right type of bikini can be obtained by mail order from any muscle magazine. Many girls buy cheap ones which they can adapt themselves, or have them made. They do not last long in contest conditions and you may find you need one or two new ones each time you compete.

Choose a colour which complements your skin tone and hair colour. Black will be lifeless in the spotlight, cut you in half and do nothing for you, while white can be fattening.

The top should have long straps which will tie on to the bikini bottom. Avoid the type which fastens across the centre of your back. This will obscure your back muscles and limit movement. The shape

of the top can be either triangular or bow-tie shaped. The triangle top will make your waist look slimmer, the other type will make your shoulders seem broader.

The bottom half can have a V-shaped dip at front and back to show the abs. and the lower back. If you choose a style with a narrow side it will make your legs seem longer. By pulling up the bottom half high on the hips and tying it in place with the long straps, you will look more slender and tall. If your backside leaves something to be desired, choose a bikini bottom that hides it and does not cut across into the glutes, so emphasizing your weakness. It is all an illusion after all!

Once you have your bikini, sew the top half firmly on to the straps at every point to avoid it slipping around when you move. Take off all hanging ties and fussy ornamentation. Make sure the strap around the back of your neck is sewn into a strip and not tied into a bow so that the ends hang down your back messily. Try it on and adjust it to look its best; then try posing in it and make sure it stays on. On the day, if necessary, use double-sided sellotape to stick the top half firmly on to your skin before you oil up. You want to be remembered for your muscles, not the fact that your bikini top fell off.

h. The Compulsory Poses

Rounds 1 and 2 of the judging consist of the compulsory poses, and you will need to start practising these at the same time as your free-posing routine, if not before, since mastery of the compulsories will enable you to create a basic sequence from which to develop your personal routine. It is a grave mistake to concentrate all your attention on the free-posing round and leave the compulsory poses to chance. The same number of marks will be awarded for each of the three competition rounds, so they are just as important to practise.

The scoring is divided into Round 1: Symmetry and Proportions; Round 2: Muscularity; Round 3: Presentation (i.e. free posing). At major contests Rounds 1 and 2 are now judged together as one.

Round 1: Relaxed Posture
You will probably be asked to perform these in a line with all other competitors at first, and possibly with two or three others subsequently. The main thing to remember about this round is that these are real poses, and no one will actually be relaxed, so do not stand like a sack of potatoes and hope to win. Practise standing with your front, side and back and other side to the mirror, and concentrate on making your shoulders appear broader and your waist narrower. Lift your chest up from your diaphragm

and expand it. Push your shoulders forward at the same time and suck in your tummy. Breathe very shallowly to avoid expanding it, and keep your chin up.

When you quarter-turn to the side, rise up on your toes like a model on a catwalk – you can sneak in a calf flex that way, and look very graceful and tall. When you take up your side-view pose, suck in your waist and twist slightly to narrow it further. Stand up very straight and tall and don't fidget. Keep your hands relaxed with the palms facing backwards.

Quarter-turn to the rear and rise on your toes as you do so. Spread your shoulders as wide as you can in this position, keep your chest up and waist sucked in; tighten your leg muscles.

Quarter-turn to the right and repeat your side pose.

Quarter-turn to the front, smile and acknowledge the judges, turn gracefully and walk back to your starting position at the back of the stage.

Remember the judges are looking for symmetry and good proportions, and not muscular development in this round. You are showing them how you have improved on your natural genetic structure to produce an athletic and harmonious physique.

Round 2: Compulsory Poses
There are five poses in Round 2, and these are illustrated below:

1 Double-biceps (from the front)
2 Side chest (from the left or right)
3 Double biceps (from the rear)
4 Triceps (from the left or right)
5 Abdominals and thighs

You will need to practise these every day for several weeks before a contest in order to perfect them. They are technically difficult to execute perfectly, and you must learn muscle control in each pose. The judges will be looking for muscularity in this round, so you will need to emphasize the extra muscle you have worked hard to build.

The sequence of five poses should be regarded as a choreographed mini-posing routine, and not as a disjointed set of movements with a complete collapse between each. Be sure of what you will be asked to do in advance and do it confidently. Don't look vague or uncertain on stage.

Take up a good position under a spotlight and start when you are told to do so. Practise at home or in a studio with a good mirror and side lighting.

Double Biceps from the front

Pose 1: Double Biceps From the Front
This pose is intended to display the biceps, abdominals and legs. Face forward. Position the legs. Take your weight on the right leg and bend the knee slightly. Extend the left leg in line with the right and point the toe. Flex the thighs and calves. Raise the arms, keeping the elbows high. Flex the arms and spread your lat. muscles wide. You can hold one arm higher than the other if you wish. You can clench your fists or hold them open and relaxed if you prefer. Look at one hand, and keep your chin up. Suck in your waist and flex your abs. Smile (if you can). Hold everything tight for 30 seconds.

Side Chest Pose (also showing side leg)

Double Biceps from the rear (also showing the calves)

Pose 2: Side Chest

This pose is to display the chest, shoulders, calves and biceps. It may be performed from either the left or right side. Choose your best side. (This describes how to perform the pose from the left side.)

Quarter-turn on your toes from Pose 1 position to Pose 2, as gracefully as you can. Adjust your weight on to your right leg and keep it straight. Lift your left hip and rise up on to your toe. Tuck the left foot closely against the right foot and press the ankle inwards to flex the calf muscle. Flex the thigh. Grip your left wrist with your right hand in an overhand grip. Pull your left elbow in to your waist hard and press it tight. Push up with your left hand against the resistance of the right one. Lift your chest up off your diaphragm and expand it. Suck in your waist and twist around to the left, raising your right shoulder as you do so, so that the chest appears to be as broad as possible. Press your right bicep against your chest to flex the pectoral muscles. Smile and hold everything tight for 30 seconds.

Pose 3: Double Biceps From the Rear

This pose is to display the back, biceps, leg biceps and calves.

Quarter-turn from Pose 2 to Pose 3 gracefully. Take the weight on the right leg and bend it slightly. Extend the left leg to the left and slightly back. Balance on the toes and flex the calf muscles and back of the leg. Raise the hands above the head, left arm higher than the right. Look at your left hand. Lean slightly to the right with your upper body. With hands either clenched or open as you prefer, flex the arms. Move them slightly up and down and back and forwards to emphasize the movement of the back muscles. Spread your lat. muscles out as wide as possible. Lean back very slightly to tense the spinal erector muscles. Hold tight for 30 seconds.

Triceps

Abdominals and Thighs

Pose 4: Triceps

This pose is to display the triceps, abdominals and calves. It may be performed from the right or left side. Choose your best side. (This describes how to perform the exercise from the right.)

Quarter-turn gracefully from Pose 3. Take your weight on your left leg and keep it straight. Extend the right leg and come up on your toes. If you keep it close to your left leg, you will give the impression of having narrower hips and waist. Suck your abs. right in, and twist your upper body slightly to the front. Hold your right wrist with your left hand behind your back and pull down hard. At the same time, press your upper right arm against your body to flex the triceps. Flex and unflex it to move the muscles. Look at the judges and smile as you do so. Hold for 30 seconds.

Pose 5: Abdominals and Thighs

This pose is intended to show the legs and stomach muscles, as well as the arms.

Gracefully quarter-turn from Pose 4. Raise your arms slowly behind your head, elbows uppermost. Flex the arms and lats. Take your weight on your right leg and extend the left. Flex and unflex the left thigh a couple of times and smile, then blow all the air out of your lungs, suck in your mid-section tight under your ribcage (this is called a 'vacuum') and finally, without inhaling, flex your abs. into the space. Sway your hips slightly to move the abs. around dramatically. This can be a spectacular finish if you have really good abs. to show. If not, don't dwell on it!

These are just guidelines about how to perform the compulsory poses. Everyone develops their own individual way of presenting them. Adapt them to your own style, but remember always to be flowing, graceful and feminine, and to give a little bow to acknowledge the judges at the end.

PRE-CONTEST BEAUTY TREATMENT

a. *Depilation*

On stage, under the lights, every last little whisker will show. Make sure you have a leg and bikini wax at least two weeks prior to the contest, so all irritation has a chance to subside. If you have a wax after you start tanning, you will end up with white patches. So de-fuzz first. Shave off any other areas that seem conspicuously hairy. Once you tan, even blonde hair will show up.

b. *Tanning*

A really deep mahogany tan is vital, for contests can be won or lost on this factor. The tan is not just for cosmetic effect. The darker colour emphasizes the definition of the muscles – which is one reason why black bodybuilders always look so spectacular (although if you are coloured, you may still need extra fake tan as well as your natural skin tone). Without a deep tan you will not only look unhealthy, but also flat.

A good summer tan is quite inadequate for the stage because stage lights bleach out the colour. Start off with a good sunbed or natural tan, and then top it up with fake tan. Then if the fake tan streaks on stage, you will not appear to be striped. Everyone has their own secret tanning formula!

Test your tan in a dry run a few weeks before your contest. Apply a coat every morning and evening for a week. Don't stop when you go bright orange. You will look bizarre in daylight, but ignore this and carry on applying tan. Since the messy stuff rubs off, wear old undies and nightclothes and sleep in old sheets for the duration of the experiment. Try to avoid bathing and only have quick showers, so you do not keep washing off the colour.

Remember it takes at least two weeks for the tan to fade. It cracks into lines and makes you look like old Egyptian papyrus, while your toes and nails stay orange for weeks. For this reason I always avoid putting fake tan on my face and use toning make-up instead.

You will need to clean your bath every day for a week after the show, while your beautiful tan gradually goes down the plughole.

c. *Make-Up and Hairstyle*

Your hairstyle should be one which does not distract the judges from your physique, so it should be attractive and feminine but not over-elaborate. If your hair is long, tie it up so that it does not obscure your back and shoulders in any way. No hair ornaments are allowed for the pre-judging, but you may add a hairband or flower or ribbon for the evening show. No jewellery of any kind is allowed, except a wedding ring.

Experiment with your make-up in advance. Remember you are going to be on stage like an actress and will need heavier make-up than you would normally apply. Use a dark shade of foundation to match your tan. Outline your eyes with a dark pencil and use a colour of eye shadow which blends with your posing suit. Accentuate your cheekbones (they will certainly be visible!) with blusher, and apply bright lipstick to emphasize your smile.

d. *Skin Conditioning*

For the last week or two before a contest, use body oil regularly after your sunbed or shower to make your skin gleam and to soften its texture. A long-term low-fat diet and last-minute dehydration can cause dryness and wrinkling.

If you have any tattoos, scars or major skin blemishes, conceal them as far as possible with make-up.

Because of the intense final weeks of training, posing, aerobics, and other concentrated preparations, as well as last-minute nerves, you may find your metabolism speeds up so much that it is hard to rest, relax and sleep. Don't worry about this. When you are superfit you need less sleep anyway, and you will burn more calories while awake than asleep! The build-up of excitement will help you to perform at your best on the day. The most important thing is to remember that you have covered every possible angle and have done your best. You are confident and ready. You can really be proud of yourself.

PHOTOGRAPHIC SESSIONS

Always try to arrange to have a really good set of photographs taken of yourself immediately before each contest. This will not only be useful to monitor your own progress, but also for publicity purposes. It is surprising how often you get asked for pictures, and a good photographer will quite cheaply print a dozen or so of you performing a favourite pose. This is much better than leaving photography to chance and having bad press photographs of yourself printed which you hate. Protect your image, and the image of women's bodybuilding at all times.

THE CONTEST

a. *The Night Before*

If the contest you have chosen is a long way from home, make sure you travel there the previous day and spend a restful, preferably solitary, night in a comfortable hotel, as close to the contest venue as possible. Do not leave anything to chance, least of all the exigencies of public transport on a contest day.

Arrive in good time, unpack your kit, and relax. Have an early night. Make sure you bring your own special food with you. Hotels can be relied upon to provide nothing edible for a competitive bodybuilder, so have some chicken pieces or cold fish fillets wrapped in foil with jacket potatoes, grapes or apple slices for your supper. Have a couple of alcoholic drinks if you like, to act as diuretics, or alternatively some distilled water.

b. *The Morning of the Show*

Have your shower and apply the final layer of tan. Eat a slice or two of apple or potato to get some carbohydrates into your system, and have a few sips of distilled water. Put on your competition bikini, plus some warm socks and a tracksuit. Don't put on ordinary underwear as you will indent marks on your skin which take an hour to fade and will show up on stage.

Pack a personal survival kit bag, containing towel, oil, a spare bikini, small scissors, needle and thread, safety pins, your EFBB membership card, money, potassium tablets, your two cassettes with posing music, make-up, tissues, notebook and biro, hairbrush and pins, distilled water in a plastic bottle, small bottle of brandy, and bars of chocolate.

Take your vitamins and a potassium tablet to avoid cramps. Then run through your posing routine for the final time. If possible, take a portable cassette recorder with you, so you can practise to your music in front of the hotel bedroom mirror.

Finally fix your hair attractively and apply your stage make-up. Then take a big deep breath and make your way to the contest venue.

c. *When You Arrive at the Venue*

Arrive early. Show your EFBB membership card, give your name, and collect your competitor's identification disc and number. Go into the hall and have a good look at the stage, the lights, the judges' seating, the audience positioning – anything that may be relevant to or affect your performance.

Find out when and where the weigh-in will take place. Keep your tracksuit on until the last minute. Try to be the first at the weigh-in, so no one sees you stripped off, then hang around afterwards in your tracksuit to watch the opposition reveal themselves. If you fail to get into the lightweight class by just a few ounces, either go for a jog or stand under a hot arc light with towels wrapped around you for half an hour and take several Vitamin C tablets (which are fast-acting diuretics). After the weigh-in, you can go away and have something light to eat or drink to give you energy – perhaps a honey sandwich, chocolate bar, or some grapes and apple slices. Keep the bulk down, but the concentrated carbs. up.

Find the changing room and somewhere to leave your kit. Don't be psyched out by other competitors flexing apparently huge muscles and making self-confident remarks. Find a quiet corner and relax. Pin your competitor's number to your bikini bottom before you lose it, and trim the edges if the cardboard is too large. Re-check your make-up and hair and visit the ladies! (I usually do this at least 150 times.) Don't strip off yet, keep yourself under wraps and study the opposition. There may be some hours to kill while the men's classes are judged, so find out when you are likely to go on stage, and if it is going to be a long wait, join the audience and enjoy the pre-judging.

Hand in your music to the disc jockey and wait for the announcement that your class should proceed backstage. Have some brandy and chocolate to help you pump-up by flooding simple carbs. into your system. This will dilate the arteries and increase bloodflow to the muscles. It will also make you feel much more energetic, relaxed and confident. You will usually be called backstage half an hour before you go on, which will allow you time to pump-up and make final adjustments to your appearance.

d. *Pumping-Up*

At most women's contests these days, a selection of weights is provided for pumping-up, but if you enter a small regional show, you can never be too sure so, if possible, take your own. Ten- or fifteen-lb dumb-bells are all you will need.

Strip down to your bikini and pump-up your muscles. The idea is to get as much blood into the muscles as possible, to increase their size and bring out the vascularity as well immediately prior to going on stage. You can use a sequence of exercises, such as push-ups, dips, crunches, flyes, shoulder presses, behind neck presses, upright rowing, calf raises. Do high reps with a light weight to get blood in the muscles, but don't overdo it, and don't pump the legs *at all* or they will smooth out, wrecking your hard-won definition. Don't go on too long, or you will be exhausted and you may cramp up. If you do, take a potassium tablet. Remember that you must have carbs. in your system to get a good pump, so don't make the mistake of starving at the last minute. Don't pump-up too early, or you'll lose it before going on stage.

Apply your oil lightly after pumping-up. Don't put on too much, and pat it gently with a towel to remove any excess. You want to look like an élite bodybuilder, not a greasy chip, and you will be penalized for overdoing it.

e. *On Stage at Last – The Pre-judging*

Judging at bodybuilding contests takes place during the day, so when you are being judged the hall will probably be in daylight and half empty, save for some interested friends and relations. There will be none of the evening atmosphere to inspire or intimidate you.

The great moment has arrived, and you line up backstage before filing on through the wings. Remember to walk tall and athletically, chin up and confident. (Don't leave on your fluffy pink bedroom slippers, as I once did.) You want all eyes to gravitate to you because of your compelling presence, so start to act *now*. Smile and look around proudly. You may be completely unnerved by the feeling of exposure, but never show it. You probably won't register the audience at all, because the footlights will shine in your eyes and dazzle you. Make sure you are standing under a spotlight, and don't get pushed into the wings at the end of the line-up. Stay semi-flexed all the time, and don't forget the judges' eyes are watching your every move.

The whole line-up will be asked to perform quarter-turns in unison. Remember to flex inconspicuously, as you have practised, and keep smiling. You will then retire to the back of the stage.

You will be called back individually to perform the Round 2 compulsory poses. This is your chance to show how well you can do them, then you will all be brought back together and each judge in turn will select two or three girls for comparisons. Similar body-types will be picked out, and they will have to do the compulsories again. Be prepared to repeat this several times. The more comparisons are called for, the better you are doing. The judges usually pick out *their* winner and second-place girl, first, and then compare the others with them. If you are not selected do not sink into a despondent, miserable heap at the back of the stage. After all, you may be so good, they have decided already that you have won! The judges are still eyeing you, and there is Round 3 to go yet. The comparisons can be very exhausting for the winning competitors, and you can relax while they are being put through it.

At the end of this round everyone files off and then returns individually for the free-posing round. The stage is now all yours, so enjoy it, and project yourself.

If your music goes wrong, calmly walk off stage and sort it out with the disc jockey. Don't scowl or fret. Impress the judges with your 'sang-froid'. This is your big moment, you have worked weeks for it, so don't waste it. Smile and acknowledge the judges when you finish.

After the posing ends, you can relax. The results will not be announced until the evening, so you can leave the hall, have a break and a snack, or relax in your hotel room. I usually take a shower to wash off the oil and dirt, re-apply my make-up, fix my hair again and change my bikini for the evening. They get really stained and filthy with oil and tan, and you will certainly need to change.

f. *The Evening Show*

The evening show starts at about 6.30 or 7.00 P.M. The audience arrives and excitement buzzes through the hall. This time the auditorium is in darkness, and the lights and music whip up the atmosphere. You may go on stage at around 9.00 P.M. Have some more chocolate and a little brandy, and then pump-up again. You will feel very tired and hungry by now, but the end is in sight!

At the show you will only be required to perform your free-posing routine. It can be a slightly longer version, as much as 2 minutes, and you can wear hair ornaments if you wish. The audience will be hyped-up, cheering, elated, and you should perform much better than you did to the empty afternoon auditorium.

This is your big moment, so sock it to them, they love it! Listen to the applause and the cheers as you flex up, hit your poses! Blink as the flash-lights explode in your eyes! This is what you have worked and starved three months for – the glamour, the thrill, the triumph. Win or lose, you'll never forget the experience. The stage is yours! As you run off you won't register the others backstage.

At the end of the individual posing, you all line up again to go on for the last time, sweaty, tired, but sky-high. The judges then call out the finalists – and you all have one minute's free-posing together. With the adrenalin flowing, the atmosphere is electric – so leap on the rostrum in front of the others, or into the spotlights at the front of the stage; flex your biceps next to hers, yours are much better! Overpower them with your own brand of charisma.

The audience howl and scream, jumping up and down in their seats, almost as exhausted as you are by the emotional tension. At last the music stops and the winner is announced. It's your name – your triumph – enjoy the trophy and the cheers – you have deserved it! A kiss from the presenter and

161

poses on the rostrum for the photographers, then it's all over. After this – you're hooked! Remember how hard it was to get yourself on stage? Now it will be hard to keep you off . . .

g. *After-Effects*

After the contest, whether you have won or lost, you can expect a big let-down. The weeks leading up to a show are an enormous strain on your physical and mental resources, and the diet of the last weeks can be punitive. Once it is all over, your body will cry out for carbohydrate, and it is very, very hard, if not impossible, to resist. Most bodybuilders have experienced the post-contest binge, a disastrous day or two of obsessively eating everything in sight. Your body will not enjoy it and will blow up with the water which is stored with the surplus carbohydrate. You will feel as if you've been poisoned. If you can discipline yourself to avoid it, do so at all costs, or limit your binge to one post-contest meal only.

The mental after-effects are probably worse – win or lose you will feel as if a steam-roller has gone over you, flat, depressed, exhausted. You will have no incentive to train and will probably hate the very sight of the gym. If you can, take one or two weeks off training. Stay out of the gym completely and do not return until you feel enthusiastic again. Gradually phase back into your diet some of the things you gave up. Visit your friends, go to the cinema, have a complete break.

If you wish, before you lose your definition, have some photos taken while you are still in top condition for your record book. Put your trophy on a shelf, and clear a space for the others which will join it soon!

h. *Losing Constructively*

If you did not win, then do not, as so many do, blame bad judging, and cry 'I was robbed'! You lost because you had faults and because, however good you were, someone else was better on the day. Regard your failure as useful experience. Analyse what went wrong and ask as many judges as possible their frank opinion and for advice on what you need to do to improve. Then go away and work on it, so that next time you win.

Six former British and International champions. This page ABOVE Carolyn Cheshire, BELOW Brenda Eppey. Opposite page ABOVE LEFT Della Shahabi, ABOVE RIGHT Carol White; BELOW LEFT Anita Pinnock, BELOW RIGHT Angela Graham.

THE FUTURE OF WOMEN'S BODYBUILDING

Since the momentous day in August 1979, when Carla Dunlap kicked off her high heels and hit a muscle pose to wild acclaim in the USA's very first 'Best in the World' Championship, women's bodybuilding has travelled a long, long way, and very fast too. On that day, beauty contests died for ever.

Five years later, Carla became 'Miss Olympia' and bodybuilding for women is an established sport around the world, with thousands of dedicated supporters. Despite the continuing controversy concerning 'muscle' versus 'femininity', the new-look woman is here to stay. Because the sport is so new, no one yet knows the ultimate potential of the female form, and what can be achieved, in time, by hard training.

At present, some people are horrified and repelled by the super-muscularity and definition of Bev Francis, but people were equally shocked five years ago by Laura Coombes. Laura was simply ahead of her time, and many others have now caught up with her.

Perhaps Bev Francis' physique is also indicative of the way things will go. Maybe she is simply five years in advance of everyone else. Personally, I hope this is not the future course. If bodybuilding were all about muscle, then she should be 'Miss Olympia' now, but other factors such as feminine proportions and graceful presentation are also involved. Some girls will always have one-in-ten-million genes which allow such extreme development naturally. The rest will not, and if super-muscularity becomes the standard, then the average competitor will have no alternative but to resort to drugs to compete. Whatever else happens in the women's side of the sport, I hope drugs stay out of it.

In my view a balance of muscularity, leanness, femininity, radiant good health and first-rate presentation should be the criteria for winning.

Couple competitions, or mixed pairs, are a new form of contest, in which man/woman teams compete against one another. This is becoming very popular with bodybuilding fans all over the world, and is now part of contests at international level. It has exactly the same appeal as classical ballet – the sensual interaction of graceful, lithe and beautiful male and female bodies.

Bodybuilding contests are undeniably part show business, but don't ever forget that for everyone involved, the glamorous end product is the result of thousands of hours of disciplined, remorseless, sweaty, hard graft. There are no short-cuts, but anyone who has done it will tell you that it's worth every minute of effort to be in tip-top shape and win!

APPENDICES

Appendix 1

THE LANGUAGE OF BODYBUILDING (GLOSSARY)

Aerobic Exercise

Any form of exercise that demands a constant supply of oxygen for its maintenance. The word 'aerobic' derives from the ancient Greek meaning 'with air'. It involves low-intensity exercise carried out for sustained periods of time within the body's capacity to supply oxygen to the working muscles. For an exercise to be aerobic, the pulse rate has to be raised to a pre-determined level, and sustained at that level for between 10 minutes and an hour, on a regular basis. Typical forms of aerobic exercise are jogging, cycling, long-distance swimming, aerobic dance and circuit weight-training.

Anaerobic Exercise

'Anaerobic' exercise is any activity that is so strenuous that the body cannot supply oxygen to the working muscles fast enough for them to convert it into energy. The body goes into 'oxygen debt' and the exercise soon has to stop. Bodybuilding training is mainly anaerobic.

BAWLA (British Amateur Weight-Lifting Association)

Weight-lifting as a sport in Britain is run by the British Amateur Weight-Lifting Association, which holds regular courses for instructors and coaches. These concentrate on weight-lifting, but also teach sound basic principles of weight-training. Diplomas are awarded after a strict written and practical examination. At present, these are the only recognized qualifications in this country. There is no recognized bodybuilding instructors' course, as yet, although the EFBB has plans to start one as soon as possible.

Bodybuilding

An international sport for men and women, whose aim is to produce a perfect physique, combining a symmetrical and pleasing muscular development with good proportions and presentation, by the application of heavy weights and special nutrition. It is the only sport in which the training techniques employed are not directly used in competition.

Burn

A feeling of heat in a muscle which has been worked to its limits.

Cheating

Swinging your body, or the weight, to help you perform an exercise with more weight than you can handle in strict form. This involves assistance of other muscle groups and is therefore 'cheating' you of the intended training effect. A bad fault for beginners, but a useful intensification technique when used correctly for advanced training.

Clean

A movement used to lift a barbell from the floor to the shoulders quickly and safely, prior to starting an exercise in the standing or overhead position. It can be a specific heavy exercise on its own, when it is called a power-clean.

Contest Condition (or 'Peak' Condition)

The achievement of maximum muscularity, combined with minimum bodyfat for the day of a bodybuilding contest. The bodybuilder seeks to appear as defined as possible, with healthy skin-tone, tightly drawn across dense, hard muscles.

Cutting-Up

Dieting to reduce bodyfat levels to an absolute minimum, in order to achieve contest definition.

Definition

Achieving minimum bodyfat in combination with maximum muscularity for a contest, so every muscle stands out in sharp relief. This condition is also popularly termed 'ripped' or 'cut'.

Density

An advanced condition of massive muscularity, when tissue is developed to a near maximum, and as hard as a rock, with a minimum of bodyfat. Density is a long-term development when naturally produced, usually seen in more mature bodybuilders and athletes.

Exercise

One specific action or *movement* designed to promote strength, power, fitness or flexibility. Also, any physical work-out or recreation.

Failure

The point in an exercise where the muscle is too exhausted to continue without assistance.

Flexibility

The range of limb movement over any of the joint complexes of the body, controlled by suppleness of muscles and connective tissue.

Free Weights

'Free weights' are those you can lift (such as barbells and dumb-bells) as opposed to 'machine weights' (such as Nautilus or multigym equipment).

Genetics

The inherited characteristics of your physique and metabolism, which determine your potential as a bodybuilder.

Intensity

Intensity is the degree of stress applied to any weight-training exercise. The greater the intensity the greater the muscle growth that will be stimulated. Bodybuilding programmes are based on the principle of gradually increasing intensity in each work-out, over a long period of time. Many special intensification techniques have been developed, primarily for use by very advanced bodybuilders who seek shape rather than bulk, and also for use in pre-competitive training.

Kit

The training clothes and personal equipment required for a work-out.

Mass

Mass, also termed 'bulk', refers to the size of the developed muscles. Mass is much sought after by all bodybuilders. It does not distinguish between muscle and fat.

Muscle-tone

The firm, lean, hard condition of a trained healthy muscle.

Muscularity

Refers to the relative amount of muscle to fat in your body. A top physique will always exhibit high muscularity.

Nutrition

The process of eating, digestion and assimilation of food to produce the ideal diet for building muscle and reducing fat.

Olympians

Elite bodybuilders who have competed in either the 'Mr or Miss Olympia' contests. Also, of course, any top athlete who has entered the Olympic Games.

Olympic Weight-Lifting

Olympic lifting is an established competitive sport for men only. It has been included in the Olympic Games since the first modern games held in Athens in 1896.

It is a contest to lift the biggest total possible in a combination of two lifts – the snatch and the clean and jerk.

Overload

The application of resistance to a muscle beyond the level it is used to handling in order to stimulate growth. The basic principle of bodybuilding, when applied progressively.

Peak

i) Ultimate condition for a contest.
ii) The 'peak' (highest point) of a muscle when contracted.

Posing

The method by which bodybuilders display their physiques at a contest. There are a number of compulsory poses for men and women, and also a free-posing routine set to music.

An individual bodybuilding *pose* is an artistic presentation of a bodypart or bodyparts with flexed muscles.

Powerlifting

Powerlifting is a form of weight-lifting and a more recent sport than Olympic lifting. It is controlled in Britain by BAWLA. Competitions are held for both men and women in this country and abroad, leading up to the World Championships. Competitions are held in various different weight-classes.
Powerlifting is based on three exercises only, the squat, deadlift and bench press. As in Olympic lifting, the aim is to lift the greatest poundage of weight, in a total of three lifts.

Progression
Gradually increasing resistance to overload a muscle, in order to induce growth.

Proportions
A bodybuilder's training aims to produce a balanced physique in which each bodypart is developed in perfect proportion to the others.

Psyching-Out
A mind-game employed by insecure competitors to undermine the self-confidence of others (e.g. 'You've got a great natural shape. Maybe when you get some muscles too, you'll beat me . . .', and so on).

Pump
To exercise a muscle so that it fills up with blood, a condition recognizable by a sense of fullness, increased muscle size, tight skin, heat in the muscle, prominent veins and elation.

Pumping-up
A short schedule of exercises designed to induce this condition all over the body immediately prior to going on stage in a bodybuilding contest.

Quality Training
Reducing the amount of rest between sets in combination with the use of sophisticated high-intensity techniques. This is primarily a pre-competitive technique, but can be used any time to break a sticking point or intensify training. It produces the best possible combination of muscle mass, density and definition.

Repetition
Or 'rep'. An individual performance of an exercise throughout the full range of movement, from start to finishing point. Repetitions are normally performed in series of between 6 and 15, which constitute *sets*.

Resistance
Weight used in an exercise, a term more generally used in connection with machine weights than free weights.

Rest Intervals
The short break taken between sets, when the muscle is allowed to recover and the breathing returns to normal. Rest intervals vary in length, depending on the type of schedule in use, and the bodypart exercised. Large muscle groups need more rest than small ones.

Rest intervals average about 1 minute, but can vary from practically nothing (in quality training or multiple sets), to 5 minutes (between bodyparts).

Ripped
A popular term used to describe a state of contest definition.

Routine
Also called a schedule, programme or work-out. The complete range of exercises performed in one training session, organized into a pre-determined sequence.

Set
A number of repetitions of one exercise group together and performed in sequence, followed by a rest interval and further sets (usually 3 to 6).

Spotter
Any experienced helper who can stand close by when you use heavy weights in order to catch, in case of muscle failure. A vital safety precaution for all beginners, and for anyone performing squats or bench presses, and for all intensification techniques which go beyond muscle failure.

Sticking point
The point in any exercise where a tired muscle or weak leverage makes it impossible to lift without help, in order to finish the rep.

Striations
When a competitor is really defined, with exceptionally low bodyfat, not only the muscles but the individual fibres will show up as lines across a muscle. These are called 'striations'.

Strict Form
Performing an exercise without cheating, for maximum stimulus and growth.

Supplements
Vitamins, minerals, proteins and other aids, taken in concentrated form (usually pills or powders), to assist growth, recovery, stamina or fat loss. All athletes can benefit from supplements, which are generally tailored to the needs of the individual and the specific demands of their chosen sport.

Symmetry
A term used in competitive bodybuilding to refer to the general outline and proportions of the body. The most desirable shape to achieve is an inverted triangle, with broad shoulders, tapering to a narrow waist and hips. The joints should be small and muscle volumes as large as possible, while retaining good proportions.

Vascularity
The prominent network of blood vessels visible on any bodybuilder with very low bodyfat, especially when in contest condition.

Visualization
Imagining the way you will appear when you achieve the body you desire. Visualization techniques, when properly and systematically applied, can be used to persuade the brain to produce the results you want in physical terms.

Warm-Ups
A 5 or 10 minute pre-work-out gentle exercise routine, to warm-up the body and prepare the mind for the hard work to come. Essential for the avoidance of injury when the muscles are cold.

Weights
The poundage or resistance used in weight-training. Free weights are barbells or dumb-bells and machine weights refer to equipment such as the Nautilus or multigym.

Appendix 2

BIBLIOGRAPHY

As you will see at once from the booklist, practically everything written on the subject of bodybuilding for women has been produced during the past few years in the USA. Many of these books are fronted by a 'star' bodybuilder's name, but are in fact written by a professional journalist. The texts of many are very similar, and it is only necessary to pick out one that appeals to you and it will contain most of the required information. There is, after all, a finite amount anyone can say on the subject.

I have found *The Weider Book of Bodybuilding for Women* by Betty and Joe Weider particularly straightforward, informative and helpful, as well as the more technical and much longer *Gold's Gym Book of Bodybuilding* by Ken Sprague and Bill Reynolds.

Most of these books can only be obtained by mail order via one of the muscle magazines. Very few are on sale in general bookstores, although a few big gyms stock a fairly wide selection. However, because they are imported the prices are often more than double the retail price in the USA.

There is only one British book on the market at present written specifically *for* women bodybuilders *by* a woman bodybuilder, and you are holding a copy of it.

BODYBUILDING AND WEIGHT-TRAINING

Anderson, Bob, *Stretching*, Shelter Publications, Inc., 1982

Barilleaux, Doris and Murray, Jim, *Inside Weight-Training for Women*, Contemporary Books, Inc., Chicago, 1978

Barnard, Dr Christian (ed), *The Body Machine*, Book Club Associates, 1982

Bass, Clarence, *Ripped*, Ripped Enterprises, Albuquerque, N.M., 1980

Bentley, Stacey, *Energy and Attitude*, 1980

Coe, Boyer and Valerie (with Bill Reynolds), *Boyer and Valerie Coe's Weight-Training Book*, Contemporary Books, Inc., Chicago, 1980

Columbu, Franco (with George Fels), *Winning Bodybuilding*, Contemporary Books, Inc., Chicago, 1977

Coombes, Laura (with Bill Reynolds), *Winning Women's Bodybuilding*, Contemporary Books, Inc., Chicago, 1983

Darden, Ellington, *The Nautilus Book*, Contemporary Books, Inc., Chicago, 1982

Dobbins, Bill and Sprague, Ken, *The Gold's Gym Weight-Training Book*, J. P. Tarcher, Inc., Los Angeles, 1977

Ferrigno, Carla, *For Women Only: Carla Ferrigno's Total Shape-Up Program*, Contemporary Books, Inc., Chicago, 1982

Gaines, Charles and Butler, George, *Pumping Iron*, Simon and Schuster, New York, 1974

Kennedy, Robert, *Hardcore Bodybuilding*, Sterling Publishing Co. Inc., 1982

Lear, John, *Know the Game – Weight-Training*, E. P. Publishing, London, 1981

Lyon, Lisa (with Douglas Kent Hall), *Body Magic*, Bantam Books, 1981

Murray, Jim, *Inside Bodybuilding*, Contemporary Books, Inc., Chicago, 1978

BIBLIOGRAPHY

Payne, Howard and Rosemary, *Weight-Training for All Sports*, Pelham Books, London, 1979

Pearl, Bill, *Keys to the Inner Universe*, Physical Fitness Architects, Pasadena, C.A., 1979

Pirie, Dr Lynne (with Bill Reynolds), *Getting Built*, Warner Books, 1984

Reynolds, Bill, *Complete Weight-Training Book*, Andersen World Inc., Mountain View, C.A., 1976

Reynolds, Bill, *Weight-Training for Beginners*, Contemporary Books, Inc., Chicago, 1982

Schwarzenneger, Arnold (with Douglas Kent Hall), *Arnold, The Education of a Bodybuilder*, Simon and Schuster, New York, 1977

Schwarzenneger, Arnold (with Douglas Kent Hall), *Arnold's Bodyshaping for Women*, Pelham Books, 1979

Schwarzenneger, Arnold (with Bill Dobbins), *Arnold's Bodybuilding for Men*, Simon and Schuster, New York, 1981

Serafini, Anthony, *Weight-Training for Cats*, Ballantine Books, New York, 1982

Snyder, George and Wayne, Rick, *Three More Reps* (Books 1, 1, 2), Olympus Health and Recreation, Inc., Warrington, P.A., 1979, 1981

Snyder, George and Wayne, Rick, *Women of the Olympia*, Olympus Health and Recreation, Inc., Warrington, P.A., 1981

Snyder, Lorraine, *Body Magic*, Olympus Health and Recreation, Inc., Warrington, P.A., 1979

Sprague, Ken, *The Gold's Gym Book of Strength Training for Athletes*, J. P. Tarcher, Inc., Los Angeles, 1979

Sprague, Ken and Reynolds, Bill, *The Gold's Gym Book of Bodybuilding*, Contemporary Books, Inc., Chicago, 1983

Weider, Betty and Joe, *The Weider Book of Bodybuilding for Women*, Contemporary Books, Inc., Chicago, 1981

Weider, Joe, *The IFBB Album of Bodybuilding All-Stars*, Hawthorne Books, Inc., New York, 1979

Weider, Joe, *Bodybuilding – the Weider Approach*, Contemporary Books, Inc., Chicago, 1981

Weider, Joe, *More Training Tips and Routines*, Contemporary Books, Inc., Chicago, 1982

Weider, Joe, *Women's Weight-Training and Bodybuilding – Tips and Routines*, Contemporary Books, Inc., Chicago, 1982

Weider, Joe, *The Weider System of Training*, Contemporary Books, Inc., Chicago, 1983

Zane, Frank and Christine, *The Zane Way to a Beautiful Body*, Simon and Schuster, New York, 1979

NUTRITION

Beverley, Bernard and Fairhurst, Arthur, *Ultimate Nutrition for All Sports*, Europa International Sports Aids Co., 1982

Cannon, Geoffrey and Einzig, Hetty, *Dieting Makes You Fat*, Century Publishing, 1983

Darden, Ellington, *The Nautilus Nutrition Book*, Contemporary Books, Inc., Chicago, 1981

Davis, Adelle, *Let's Eat Right to Keep Fit*, Unwin Paperbacks, London, 1979

Hunter, Carol, *Vitamins, What they are and why we need them*, Thorsons Publishers, 1978

Mervyn, Len, *Minerals and Your Health*, George Allen and Unwin, London, 1980

Ministry of Agriculture and Fisheries, *Manual of Nutrition*, HMSO, London, 1982

Neve, Pat, *Pat Neve's Bodybuilding Diet Book*, Phoenix Books, Phoenix, A.Z., 1980

Polunin, Miriam, *The Right Way to Eat*, Granada Publishing Ltd., London, 1980

Weider, Joe, *Bodybuilding Nutrition and Training Programs*, Contemporary Books, Inc., Chicago, 1981

Weider, Joe, *More Bodybuilding Nutrition and Training Programs,* Contemporary Books, Inc., Chicago, 1982

Wright, Michael, *The Salt Counter*, Pan Books, London, 1984

ADDRESSES

English Federation of Bodybuilders: Women's
Representative:
   Carolyn Cheshire,
   27 Ailsa Rd.,
   St Margaret's,
   Middlesex.

International Federation of Bodybuilders:
   2875 Bates Rd.,
   Montreal,
   P2H351B7,
   Canada.

American Federation of Women Bodybuilders:
   Doris Barilleaux,
   Box 937,
   Riverview,
   Fl. 33569
   USA.